The INTERNATIONAL LIBRARY of MUSIC

for HOME AND STUDIO

REHEARSING A DUET
From the Painting by F. Simm

THE INTERNATIONAL LIBRARY OF MUSIC

Including many of the compositions edited by
IGNACE J. PADEREWSKI
*Reprinted from the original plates of
his Century Library of Music*

Piano Series

ADVISORY BOARD ON MUSICAL PUBLICATIONS

RUDOLPH GANZ
President, Chicago Musical College

EDWIN HUGHES
Virtuoso and Teacher

THOMAS TAPPER, LITT.D.
New York Institute of Musical Art

J. LAWRENCE ERB
Connecticut College for Women

KATE S. CHITTENDEN
Dean of Music, Vassar College

A. MADELEY RICHARDSON, Mus. Doc. Oxon.
Julliard School of Music

CHARLES DENNÉE
New England Conservatory of Music

G. ACKELEY BROWER
Cadek Conservatory of Music

GEORGE FOLSOM GRANBERRY
Granberry School of Music

LEO C. MILLER
Miller Music Studios

F. CAMPBELL-WATSON, M.A.
Managing Editor

Associate and Contributing Editors for Musical Publications

FRANZ C. BORNSCHEIN   AUGUST FRAEMCKE   GUSTAV L. BECKER
HENRY HOLDEN HUSS   FELIX BOROWSKI
ARTHUR FOOTE   SIDNEY SILBER

VOLUME VI

PIANOFORTE COMPOSITIONS

THE UNIVERSITY SOCIETY
INCORPORATED
NEW YORK

Copyright, 1934 by
THE UNIVERSITY SOCIETY
INCORPORATED

In addition to a wealth of new material, this new edition of The International Library of Music combines the best features of its highly successful predecessors; namely:

Famous Songs and Those Who Made Them	Copyright 1896
The World's Best Music	Copyright 1897
Paderewski—Century Library of Music	Copyright 1900
Modern Music and Musicians	Copyright 1912
La Mejor Musica del Mundo	Copyright 1917
The University Course of Music Study	Copyright 1920
The International Library of Music	Copyright 1925
A Melhor Musica do Mundo	Copyright 1930

MANUFACTURED IN THE U. S. A.

TABLE OF CONTENTS
VOLUME SIX

		PAGE
Impromptu, Op. 90	Franz Schubert	1521
Polonaise, Op. 26, No. 1	F. Chopin	1532
Valse Fantastique	Alexandre Glazounoff	1537
Kamennoi-Ostrow, Op. 10, No. 22	Anton Rubinstein	1544
Troika en Traineaux, Op. 37, No. 11	P. Tschaikowsky	1551
Hungarian Dance No. 1, *G minor*	Johannes Brahms	1556
Hungarian Dance No. 2, *F major*	Johannes Brahms	1562
Hungarian Dance No. 3, *E major*	Johannes Brahms	1565
Hungarian Dance No. 5, *G minor*	Johannes Brahms	1569
Sunday Morning At Glion, Op. 139, No. 1	Franz Bendel	1573
Prelude, Op. 28, No. 17	F. Chopin	1578
Prelude, Op. 9, No. 1	Alexander Scriabine	1582
Tango Burlesco, Op. 28	Luis Levy	1584
Caprice, Op. 79a, No. 4b	Max Reger	1590
Caprice, Op. 43, No. 4	Anton Arensky	1592
Arabesque, Op. 45, No. 1	Theodore Leschetizky	1596
Rondo Capriccioso, Op. 14	F. Mendelssohn	1600
Waltzes, Op. 39	Johannes Brahms	1613

    1. Poco sostenuto, *E minor*   6. Poco scherzando, *G major*
    2. Grazioso, *E major*   7. Alla Zingara, *B minor*
    3. Andante espressivo, *C-sharp*   8. Moderato, *E major*
    4. Moderato, *B-flat*   9. Molto espressivo, *C-sharp minor*
    5. Espressivo, *D minor*   10. Moderato assai, *E major*

Barcarolle, *G major*, No. IV	Anton Rubinstein	1623
Barcarolle, *F minor*, Op. 30, No. 1	Anton Rubinstein	1628
Seguidilla	I. Albeniz	1634
Witches' Dance, Op. 17, No. 2	Edward MacDowell	1640
Prelude, Op. 32, No. 11	S. Rachmaninoff	1650
Humoreske, Op. 10, No. 5	S. Rachmaninoff	1653
Prelude, Op. 28, No. 1	F. Chopin	1662
Prelude, Op. 28, No. 3	F. Chopin	1663
Prelude, Op. 28, No. 16	F. Chopin	1665
Prelude, Op. 28, No. 21	F. Chopin	1670
Six Poems After Heine	Edward MacDowell	1672
I. The Fisher's Cottage		1672
II. Scotch Poem		1675
III. My Child We Once Were Children		1679
IV. In the Post-Chaise		1682
V. The Shepherd Boy		1687
VI. Death		1690
Valse Lente	Leo Delibes	1694
Intermezzo, from "Nailia"	Leo Delibes	1698

TABLE OF CONTENTS

		PAGE
Impromptu, Op. 28, No. 2	Hugo Reinhold	1706
Fugue, *E minor*	G. F. Handel	1711
Italian Concerto	J. S. Bach	1718
Autômne, Op. 35, No. 2	C. Chaminade	1736
Valse, Op 42	F. Chopin	1746
Invitation to the Dance, Op. 65	Carl M. von Weber	1756
In the Garden, at Play, Op. 97, No. 3	H. Villa-Lobos	1764
Prelude, Op. 23, No. 5	S. Rachmaninoff	1770
Sonata "Pathetique," Op. 13	L. van Beethoven	1777
Sonata "Quasi una Fantasia," Op. 27, No. 2	L. van Beethoven	1800
Nocturne, Op. 37, No. 2	F. Chopin	1819

IMPROMPTU
C MINOR

From the Century Library of Music
Edited by Ignace J. Paderewski

SCHUBERT
Op. 90

Allegro molto moderato

ten.
ff
Ped.
sf
p
pp
legatissimo
legato sempre
simile
mf
decresc.

1523

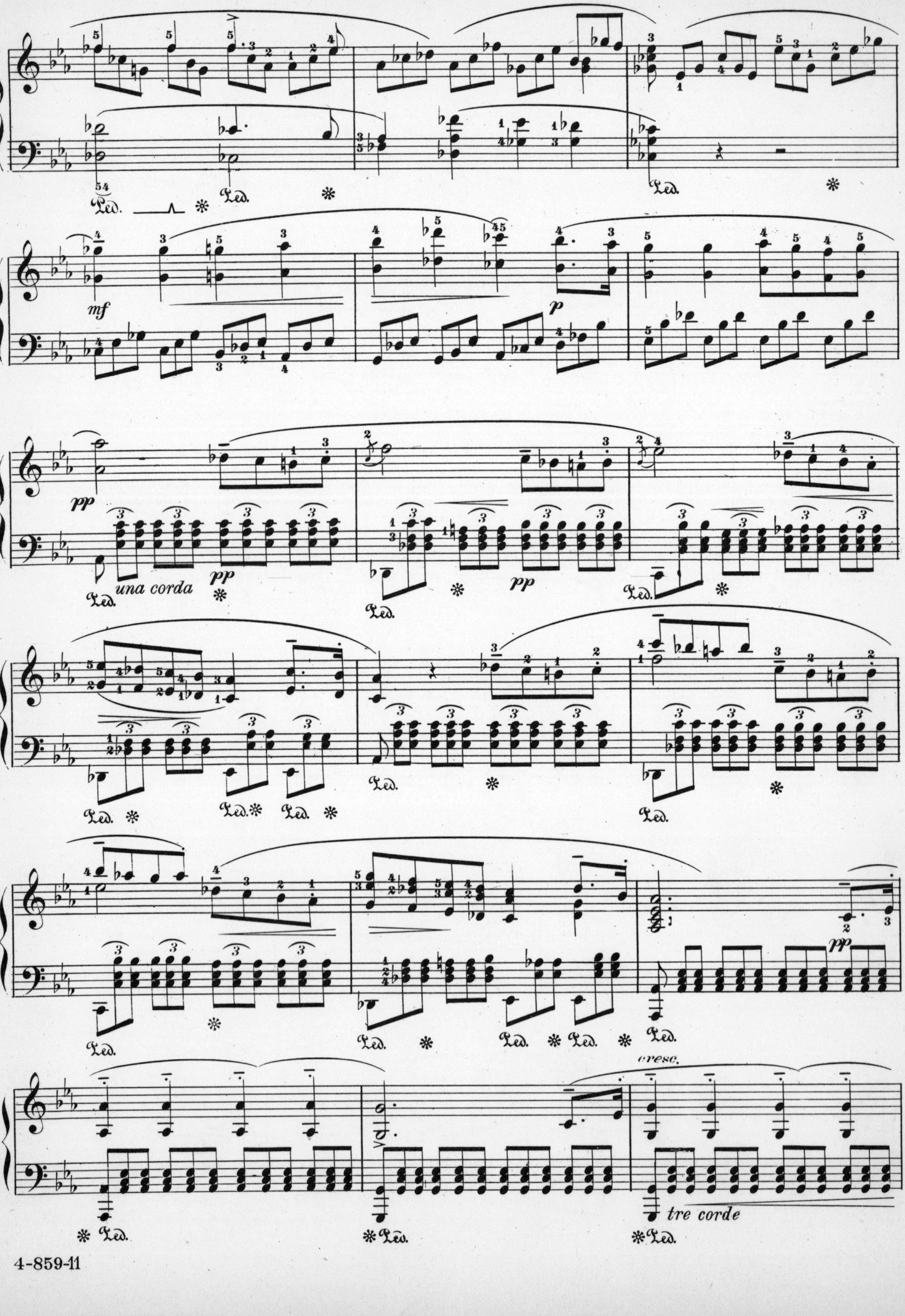
mf
p
pp
una corda
pp
pp
cresc.
tre corde

1525

1526

1527

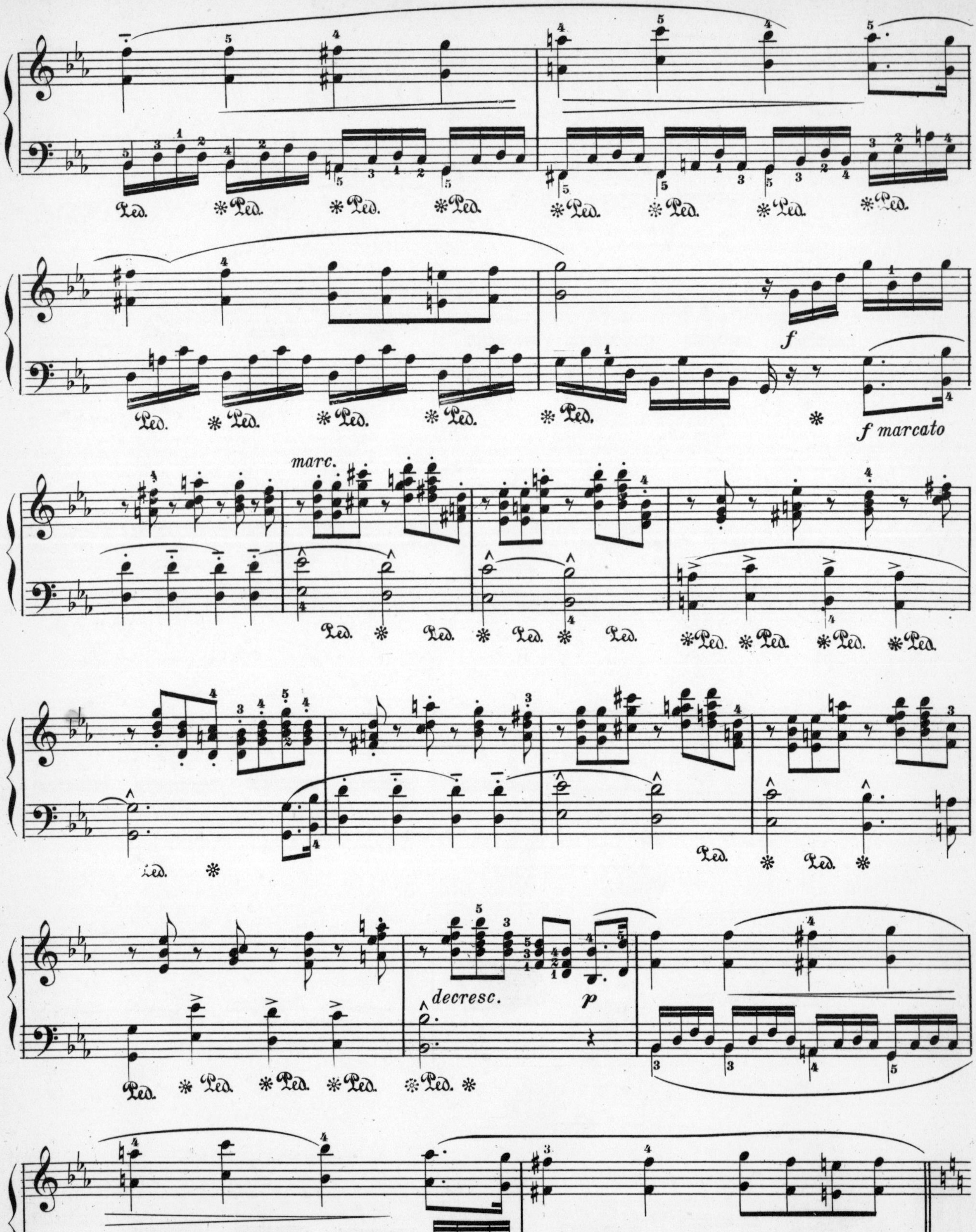
Ped.
f
f marcato
marc.
decresc.
p

1529

1530

1531

POLONAISE
C-SHARP MINOR

Edited by Charles Dennée

CHOPIN
Op. 26, No. 1

Allegro appassionato

1533

Meno mosso
semplice
p con anima
simile
f
riten.
p
a tempo
senza rigore
dolciss.
ten.
poco rubato
senza rigore
p
poco rit.
Ped.
p a tempo
indeciso

1535

1536

VALSE FANTASTIQUE
From the Ballet "RAYMONDA" Op. 57

ALEXANDRE GLAZOUNOFF

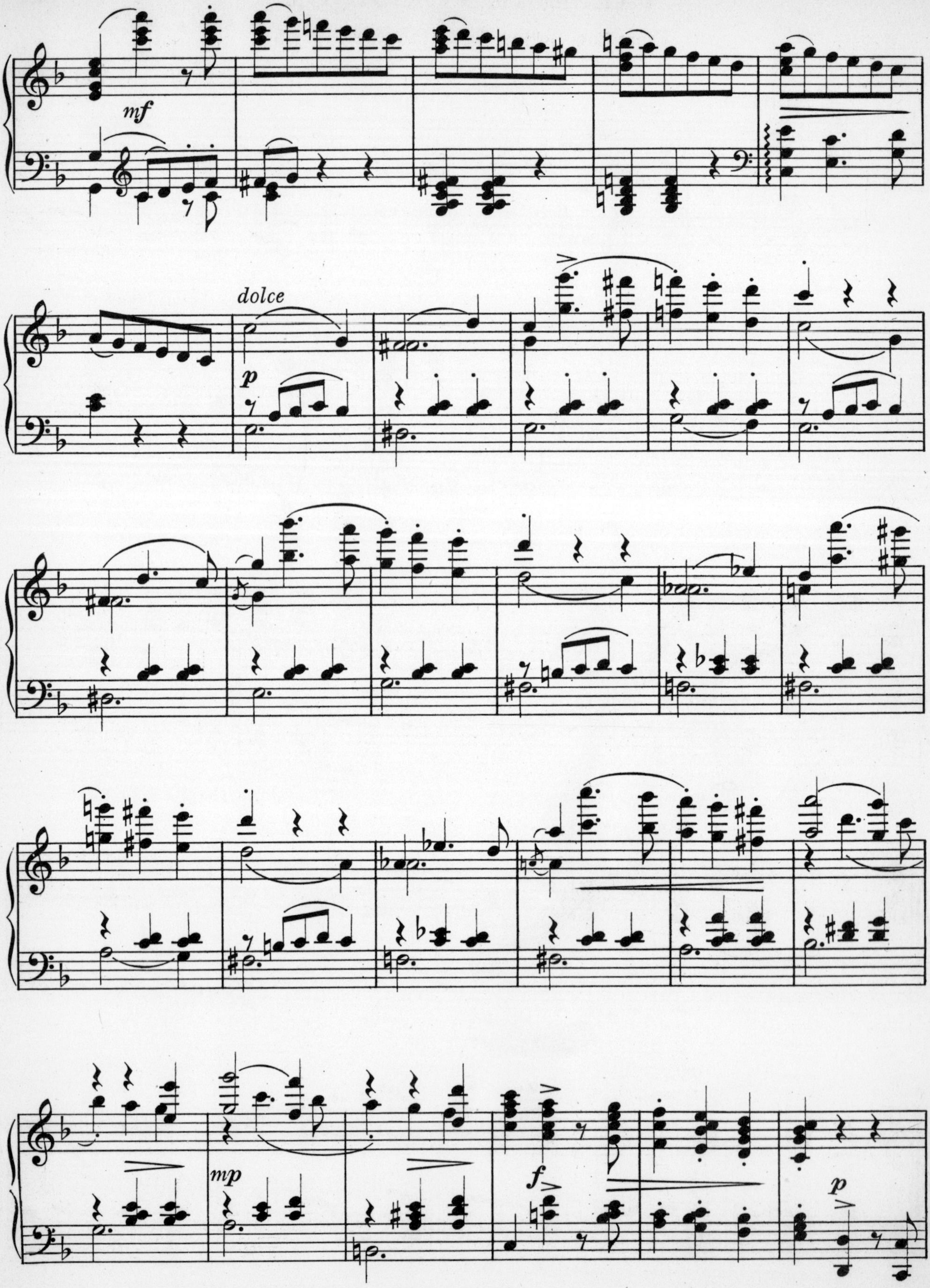
mf
dolce
p
mp
f
p

1539

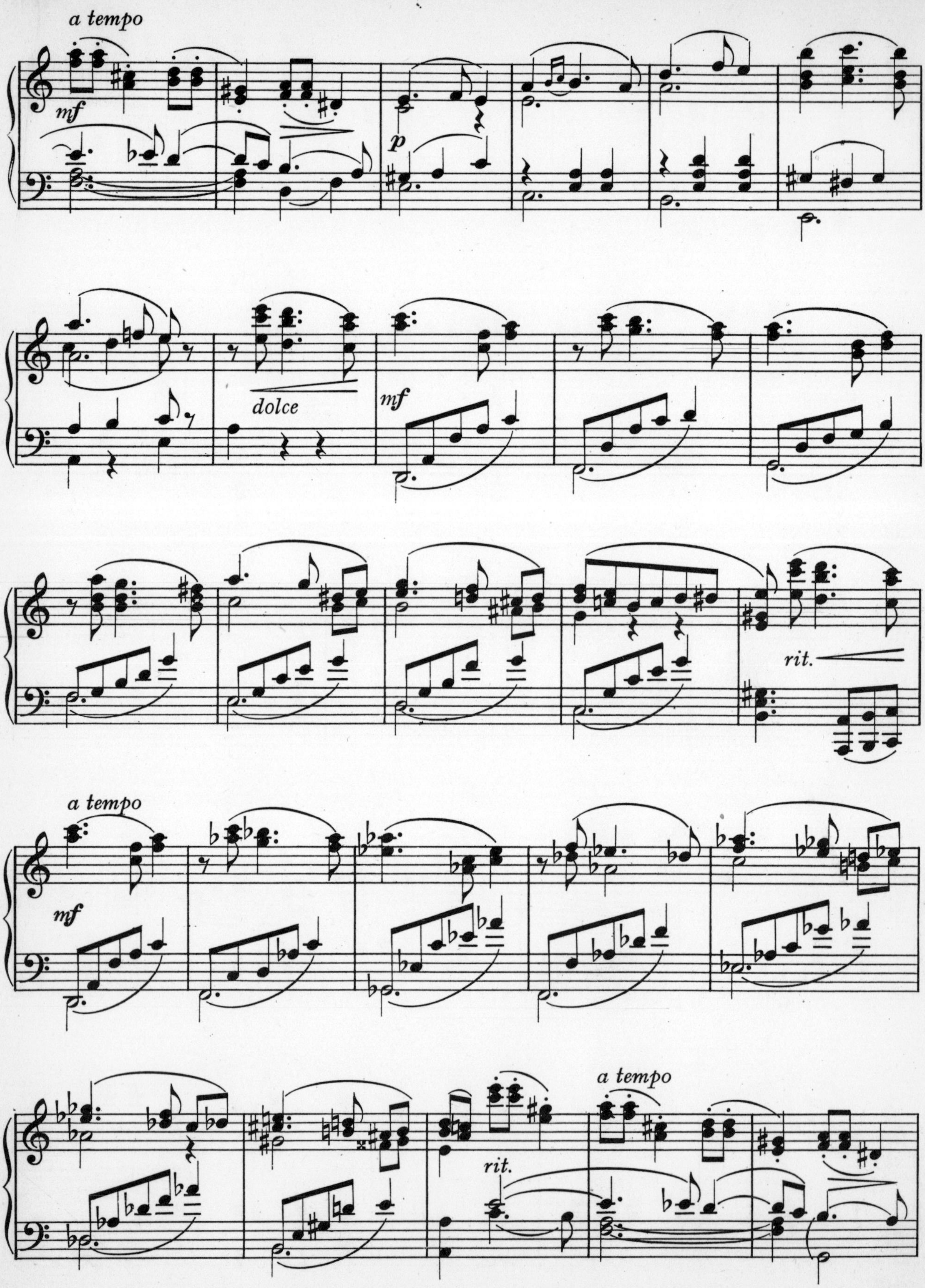
a tempo
mf
p
dolce
mf
rit.
a tempo
mf
rit.
a tempo

1541

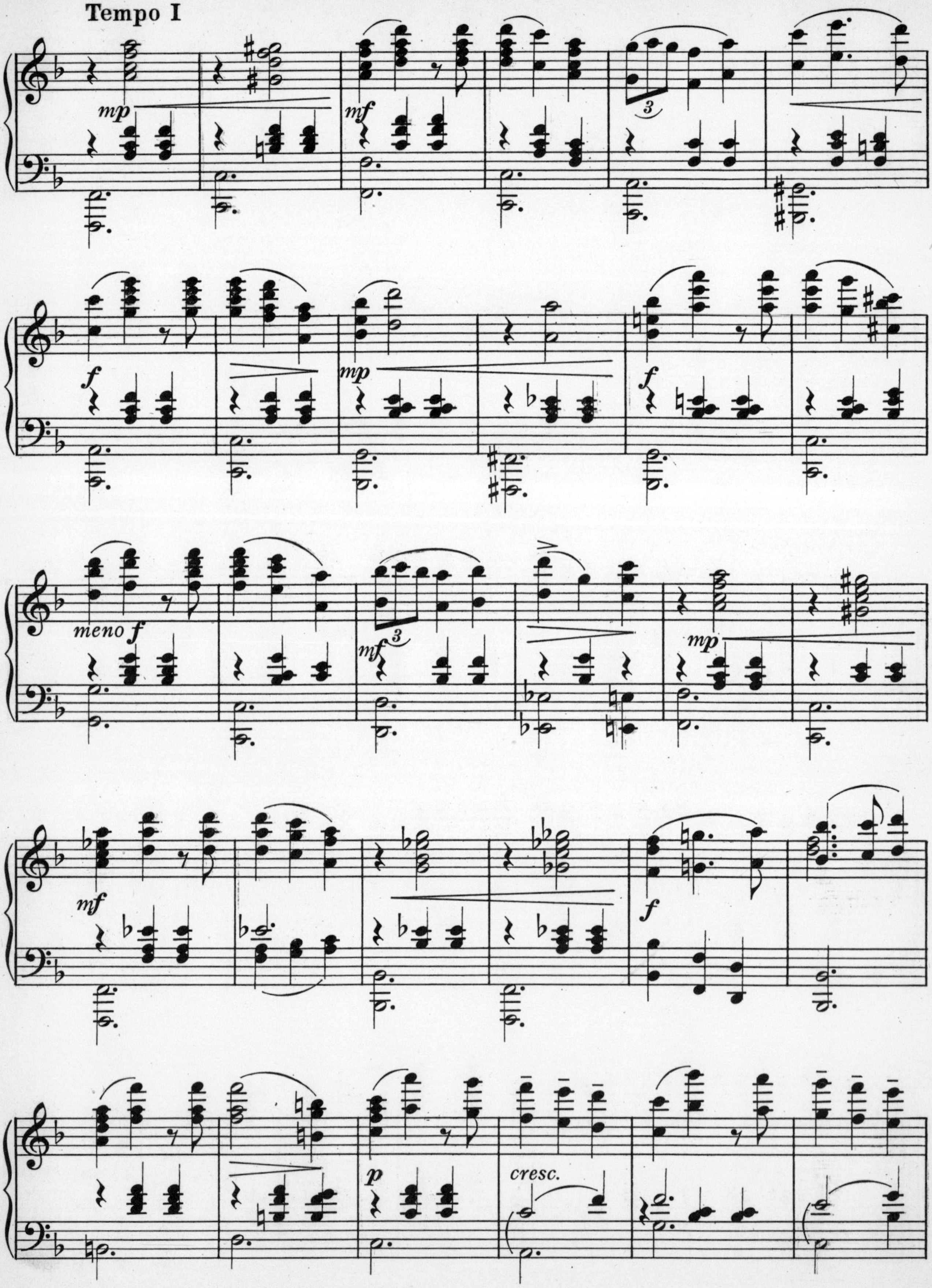
Tempo I
mp
mf
f
mp
f
meno f
mf
mp
mf
f
p
cresc.

1543

RÊVE ANGÉLIQUE
("KAMENNOI-OSTROW")

Moderato

A. RUBINSTEIN.
Op. 10, No. 22

p sempre legato

1545

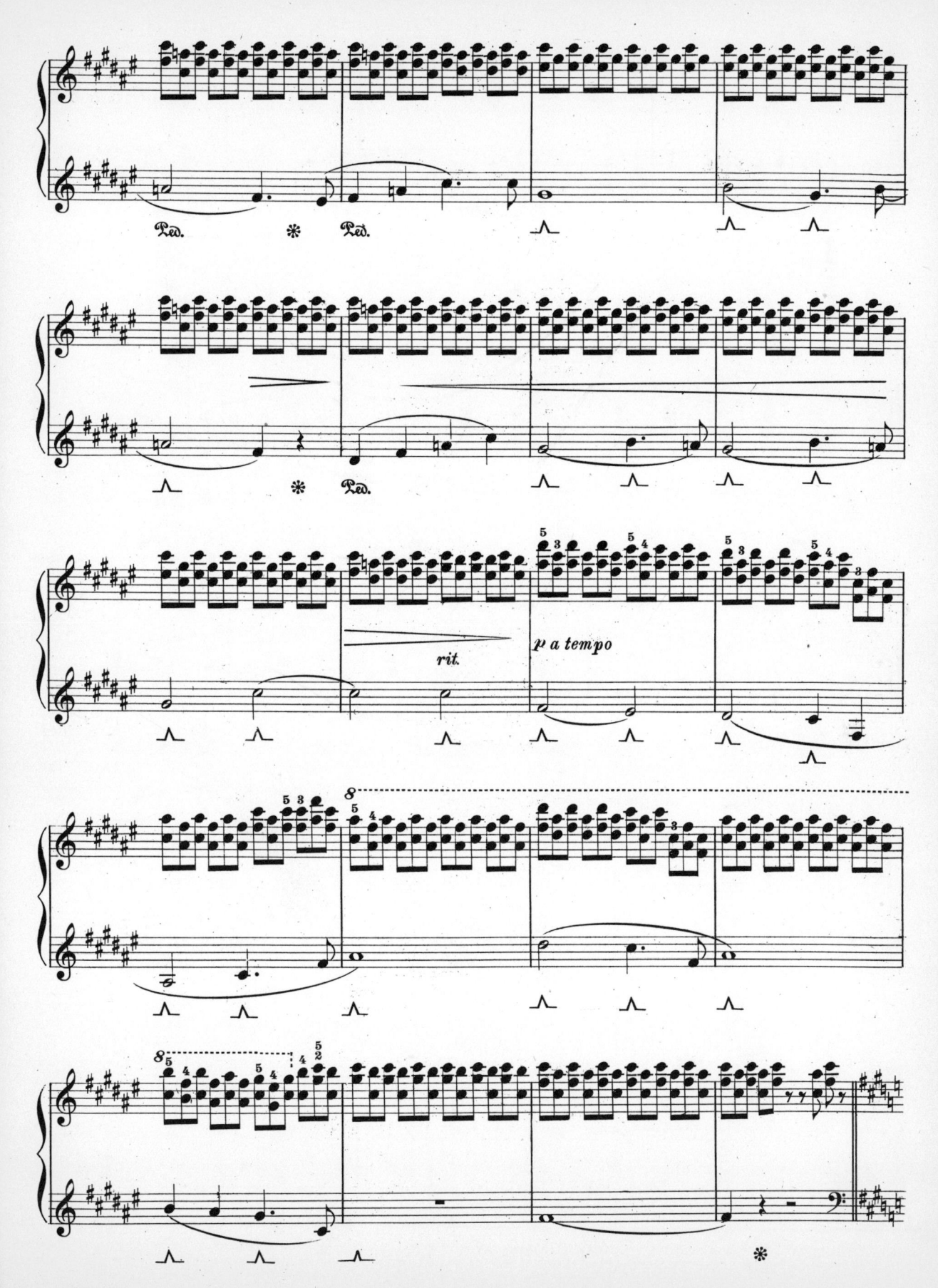

1546

Tempo I.

1548

1549

1550

TROIKA EN TRAINEAUX

Edited by
CHARLES DENNÉE

TSCHAIKOWSKY
Op. 37. No. 11

Allegro moderato

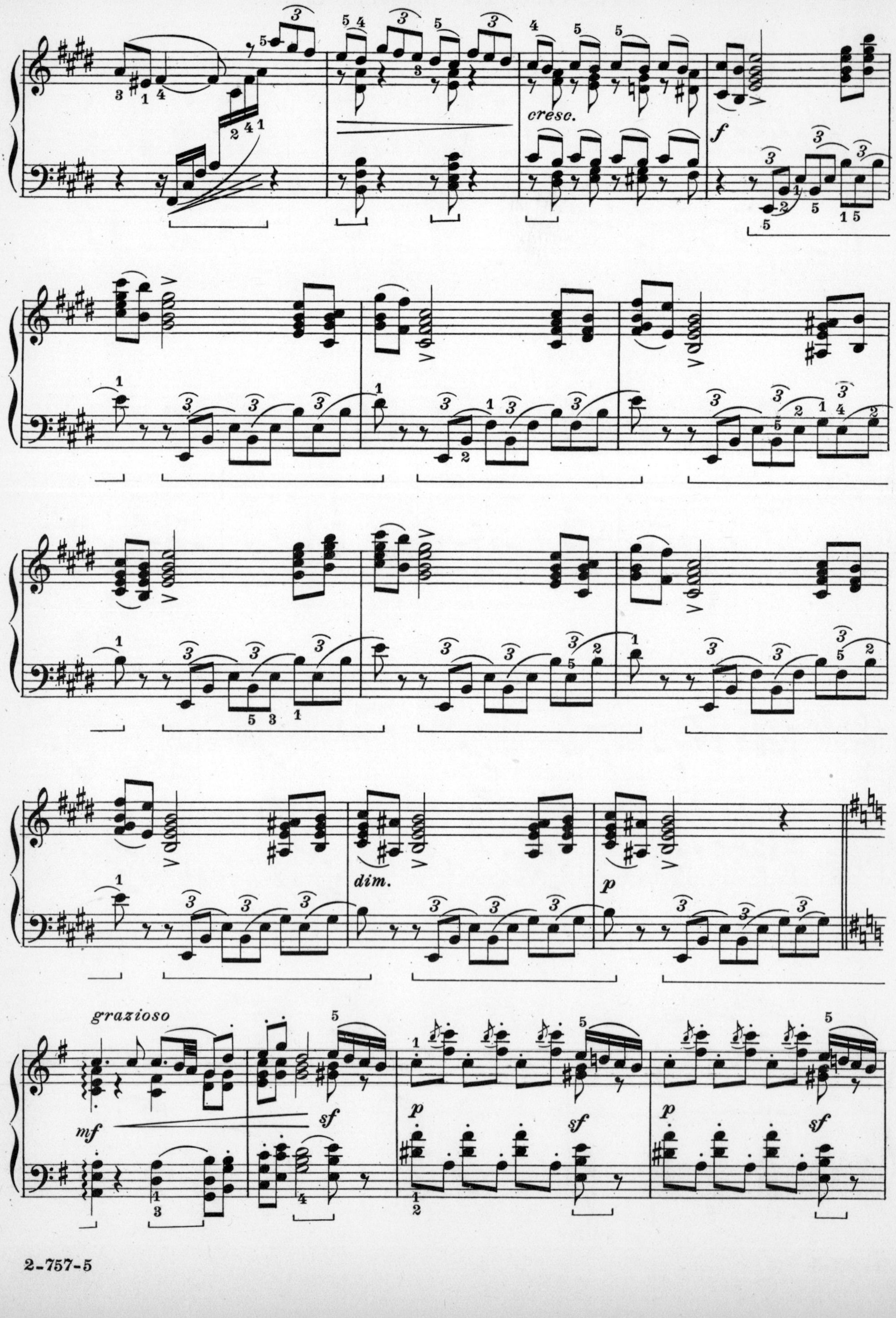
cresc.
f
dim.
p
grazioso
mf
sf
p
sf
p
sf

1553

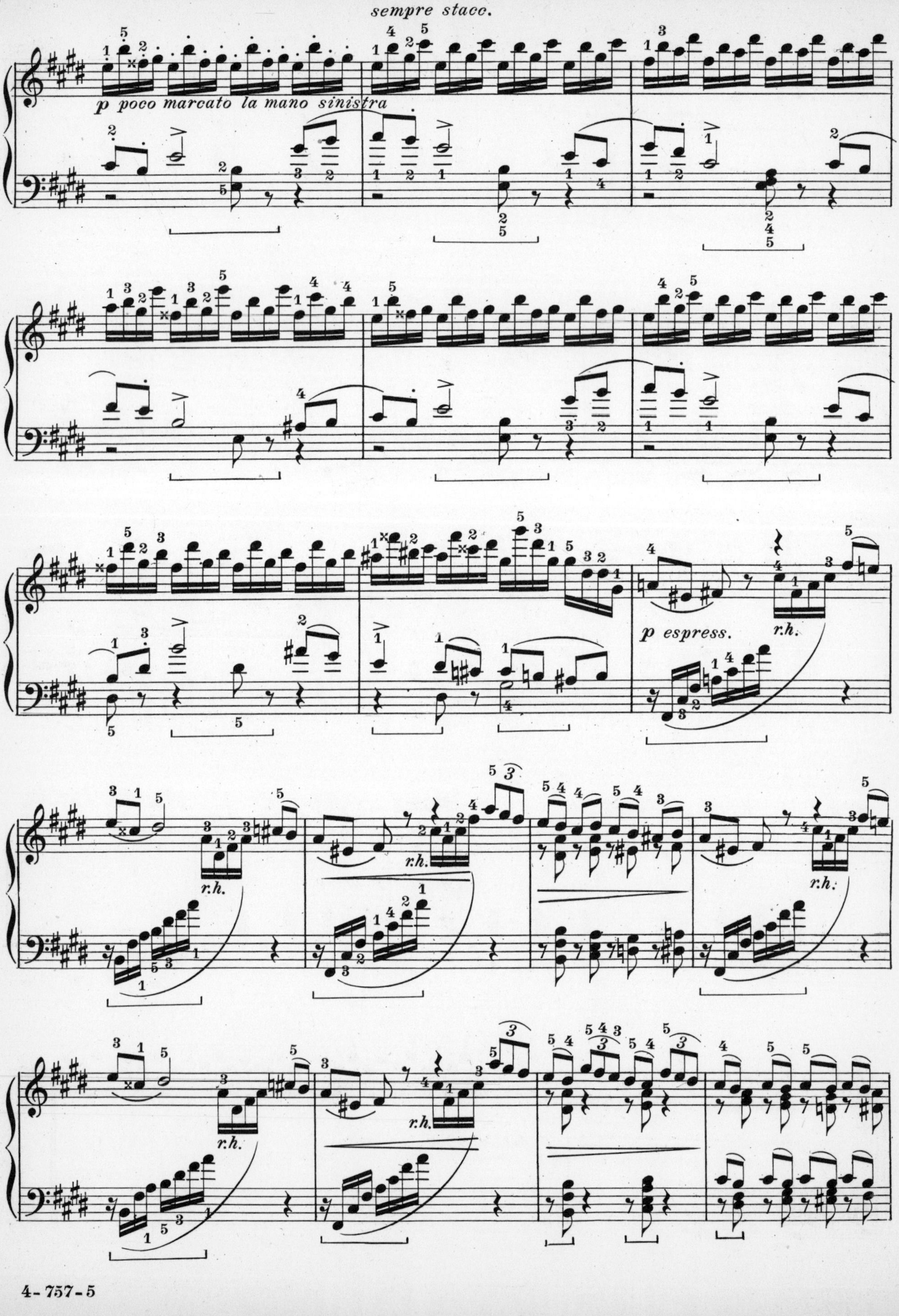
sempre stacc.
p poco marcato la mano sinistra
p espress.
r.h.

1555

THREE HUNGARIAN DANCES
No. I, in G MINOR

Edited by Charles Dennée

JOH. BRAHMS

Allegro

1557

1558

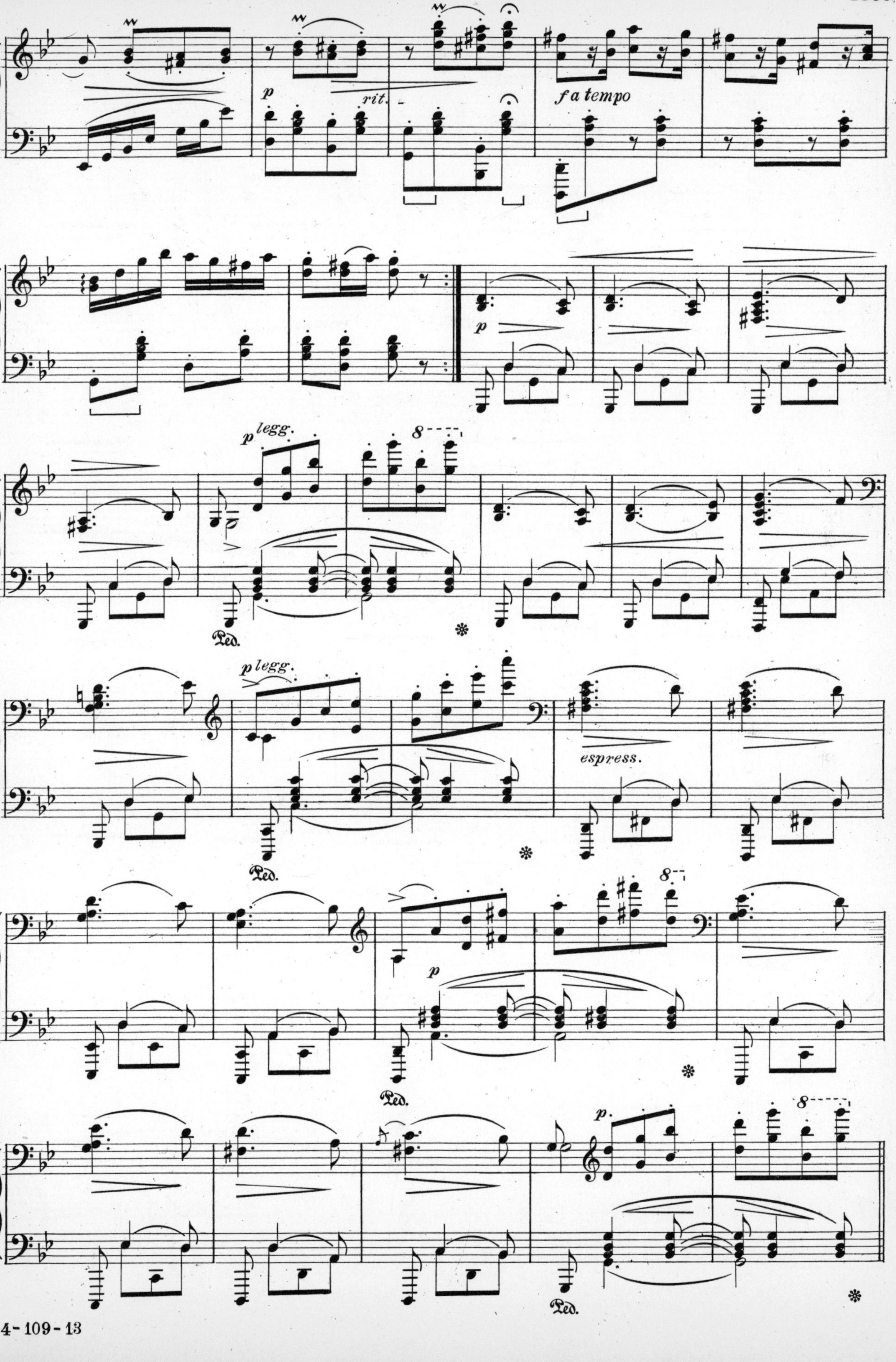
p
rit.
f a tempo
p
p legg.
8
Ped.
p legg.
Ped.
espress.
p
8
Ped.
p.
8
Ped.

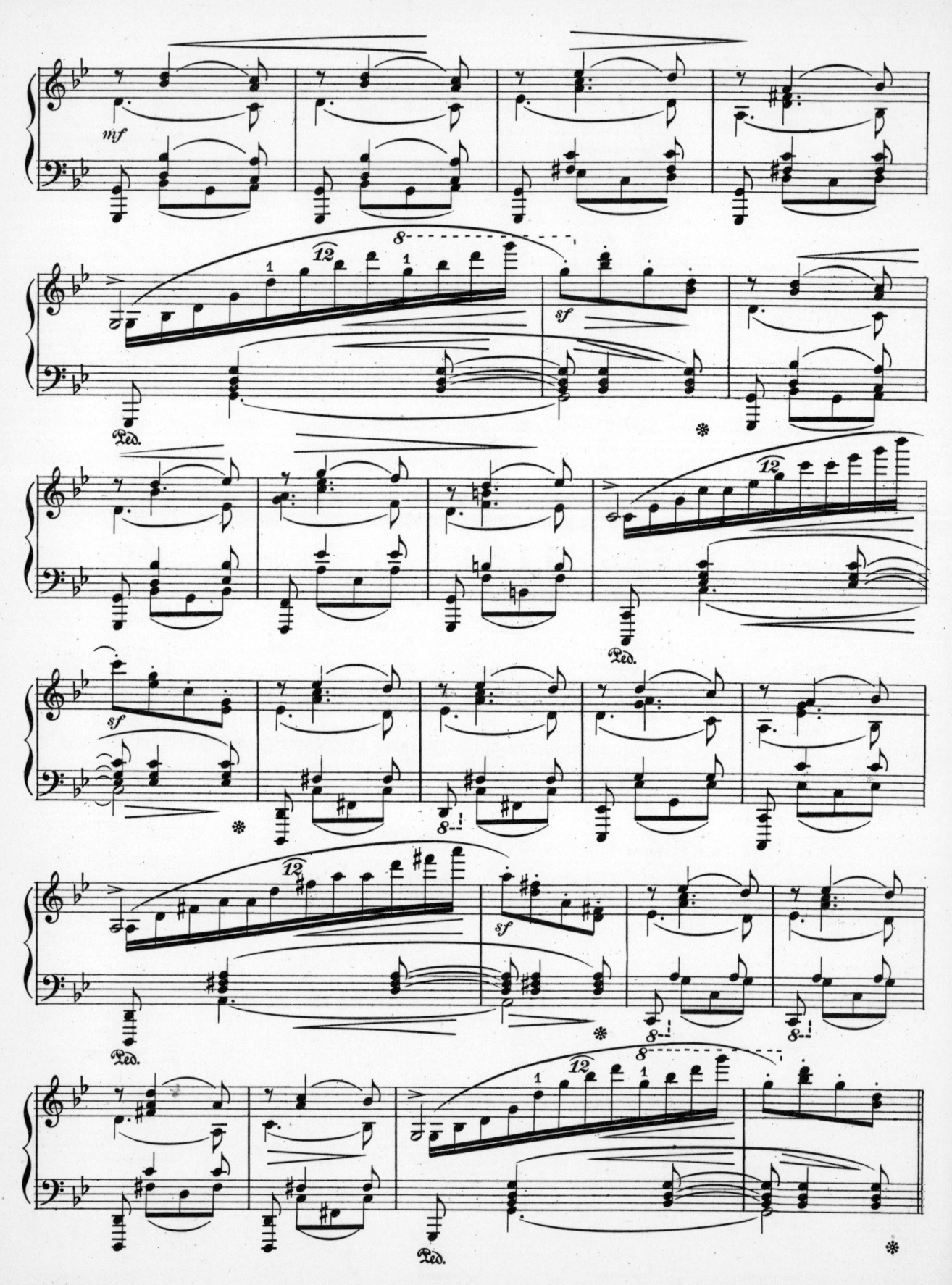
mf
sf
Ped.
sf
Ped.
sf
Ped.
Ped.

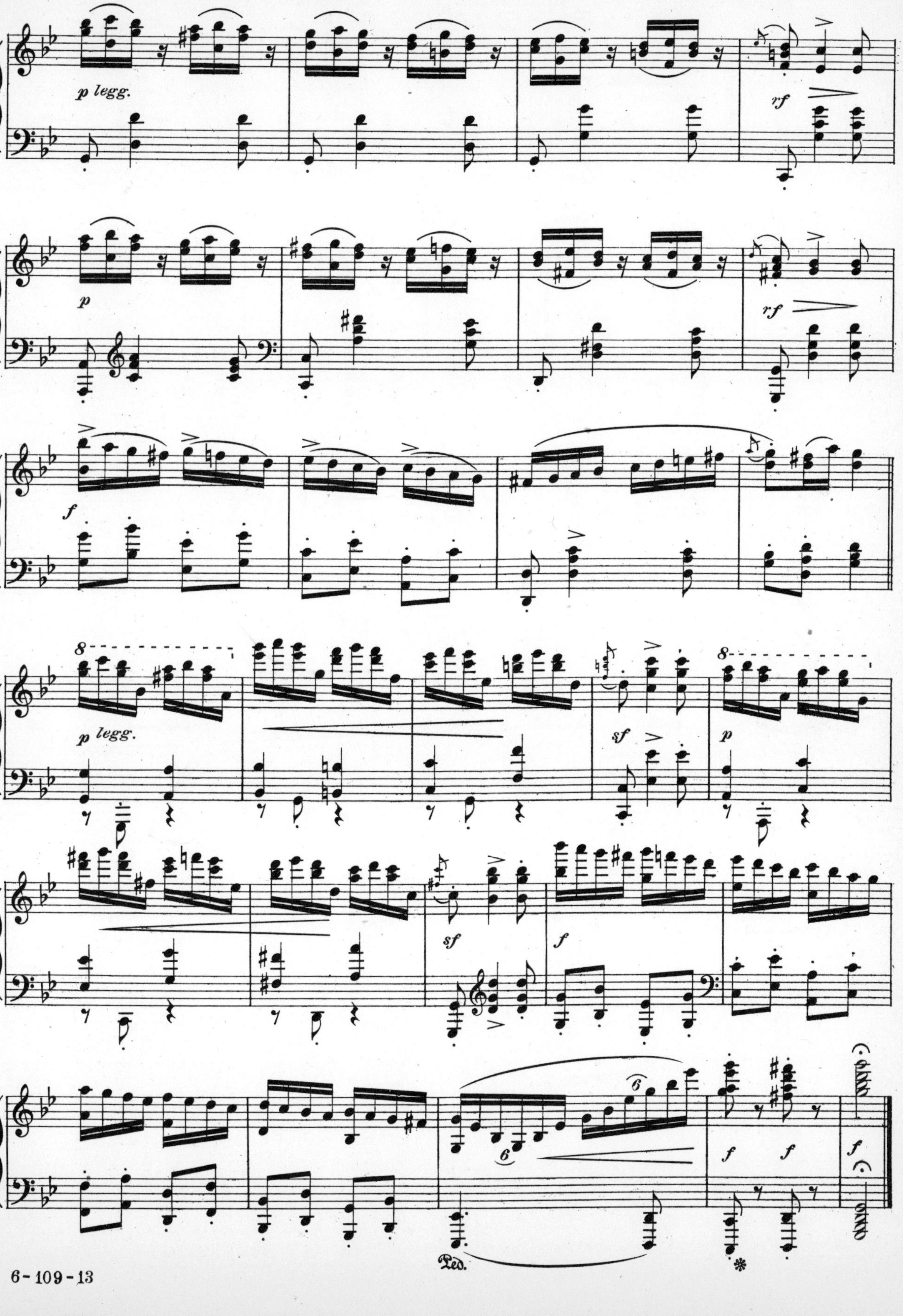
p legg.
rf
p
rf
f
8
p legg.
sf
8
p
sf
f
6
6
f
f
f
Ped.

No. II, in F MAJOR

Allegretto

1563

1564

Nº III, in E MAJOR

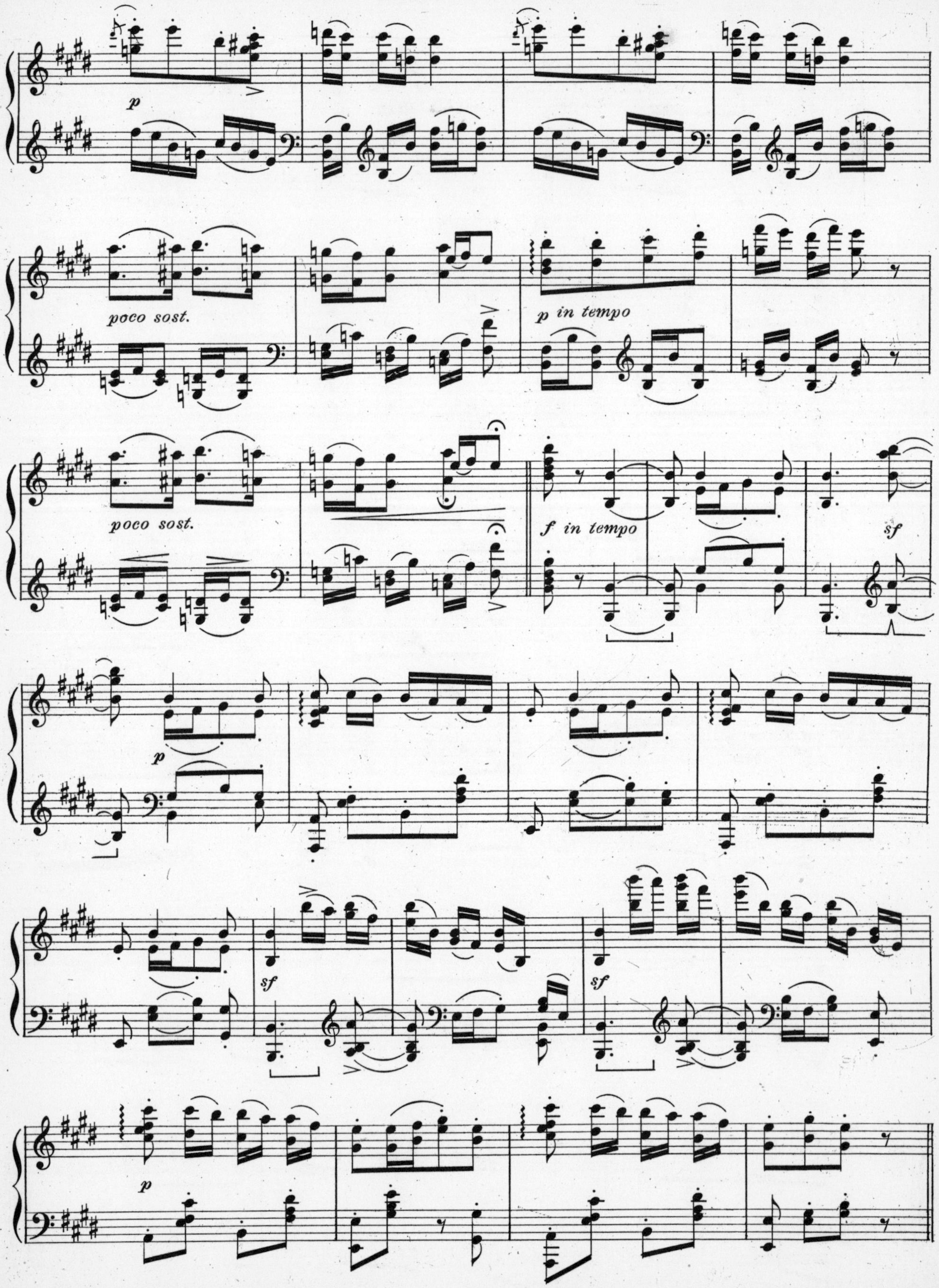
p
poco sost.
p in tempo
poco sost.
f in tempo
sf
p
sf
sf
p

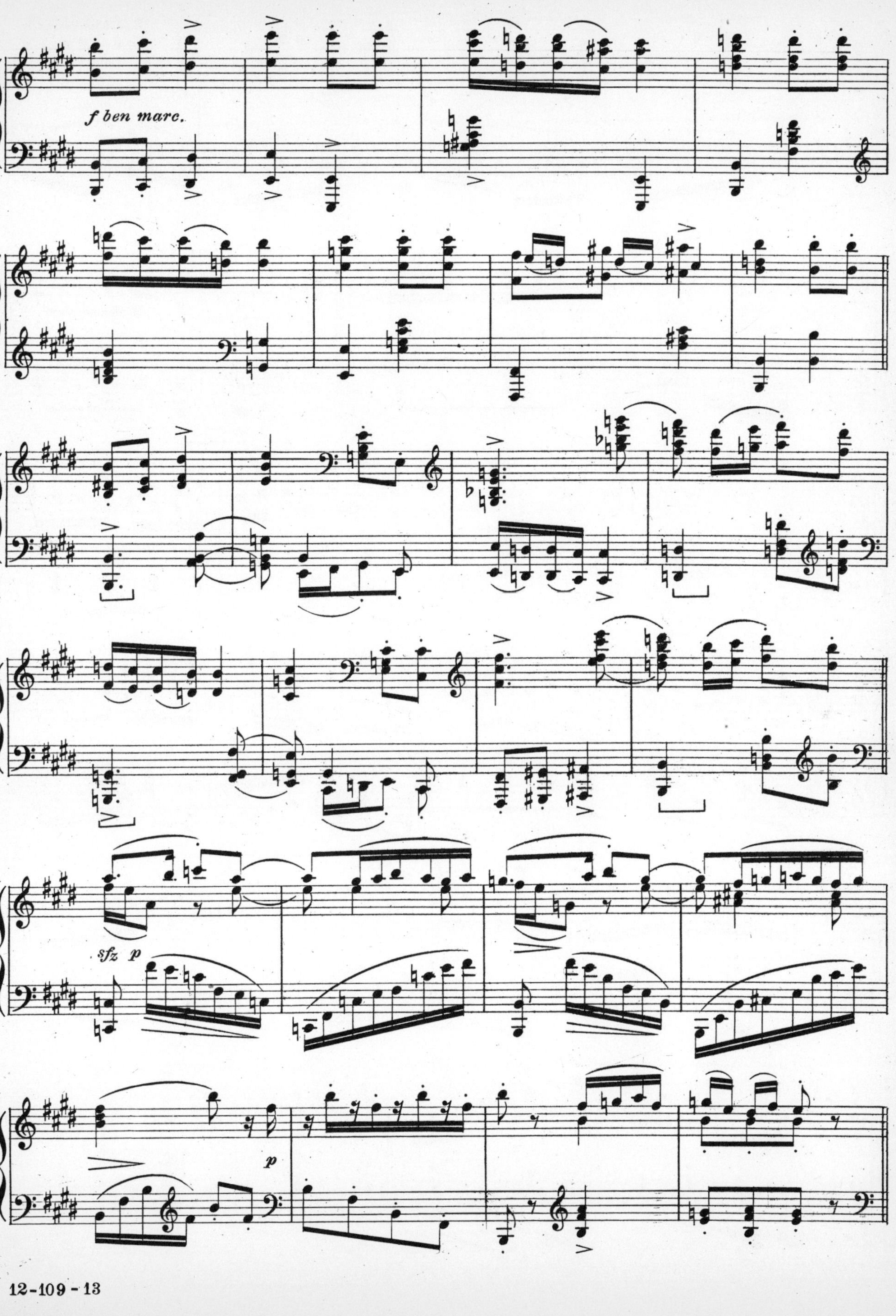
f ben marc.
sfz p
p

1568

HUNGARIAN DANCE No. V

JOHANNES BRAHMS

Allegro

1570

1571

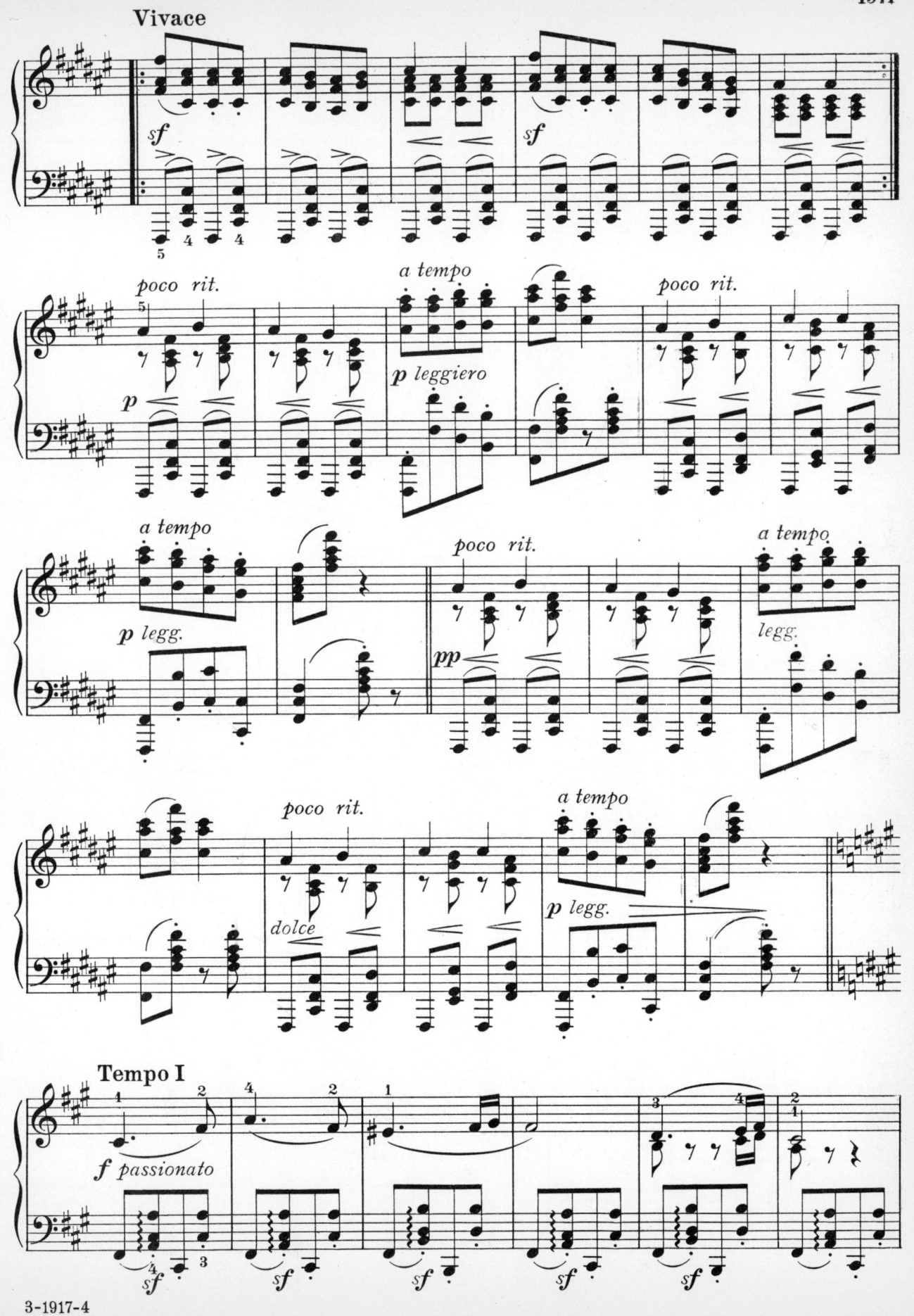

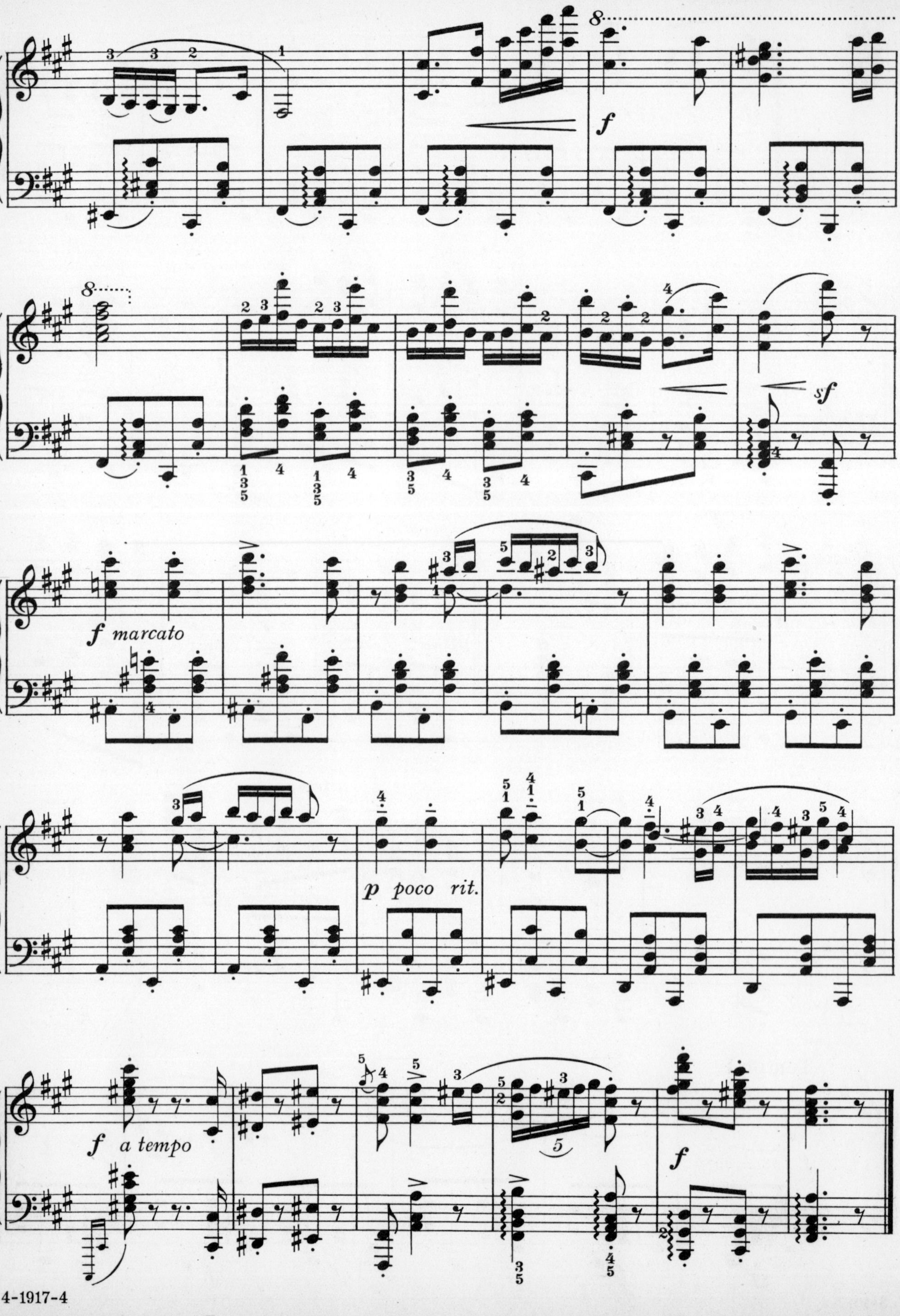
f
sf
f marcato
p poco rit.
f a tempo
f

SUNDAY MORNING AT GLION
From "AM GENFER SEE"

BENDEL
Op. 139, No. 1

1574

1575

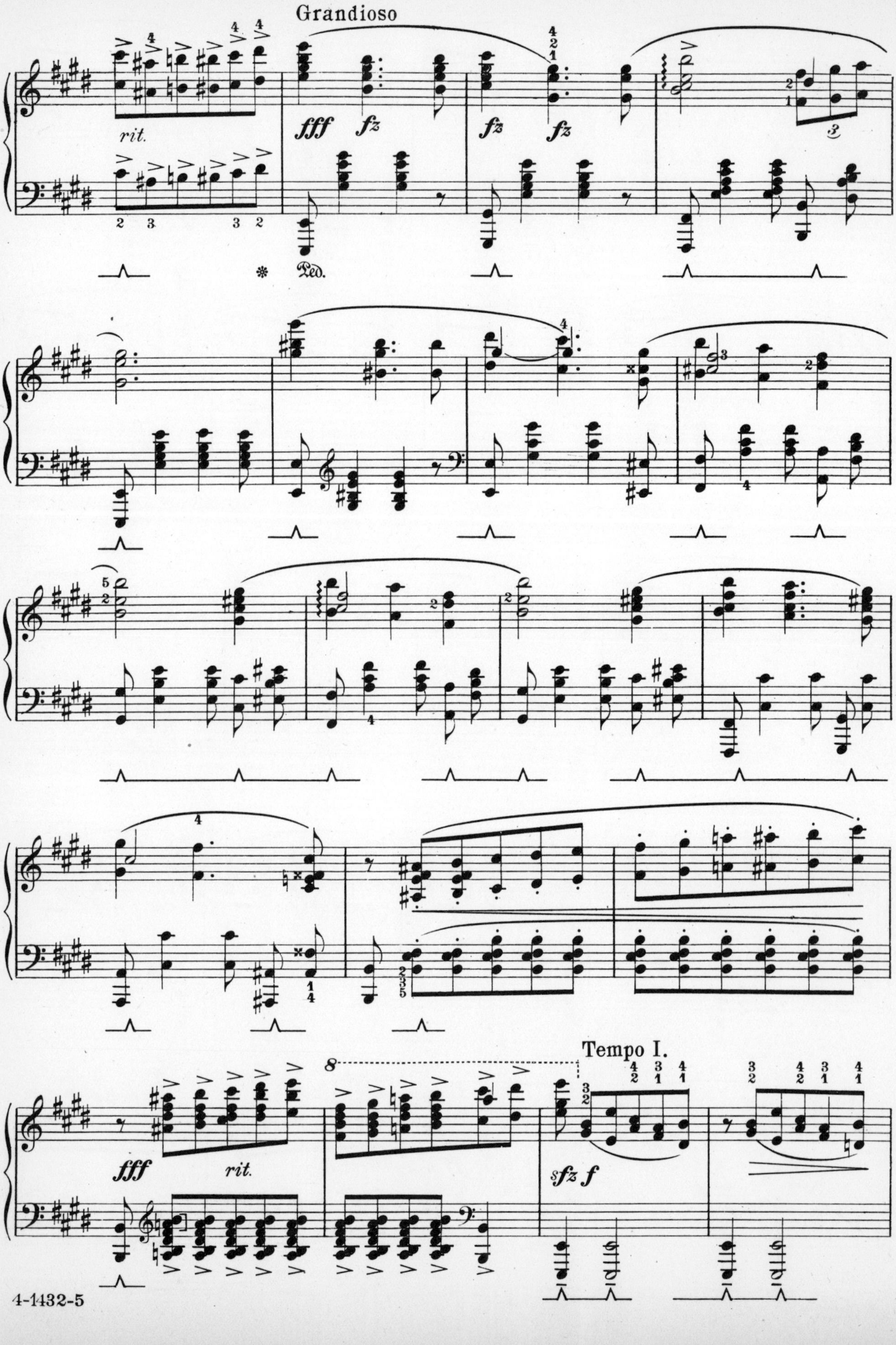
Grandioso
rit.
fff
fz
fz
fz
Ped.
8
fff
rit.
Tempo I.
sfz f

1577

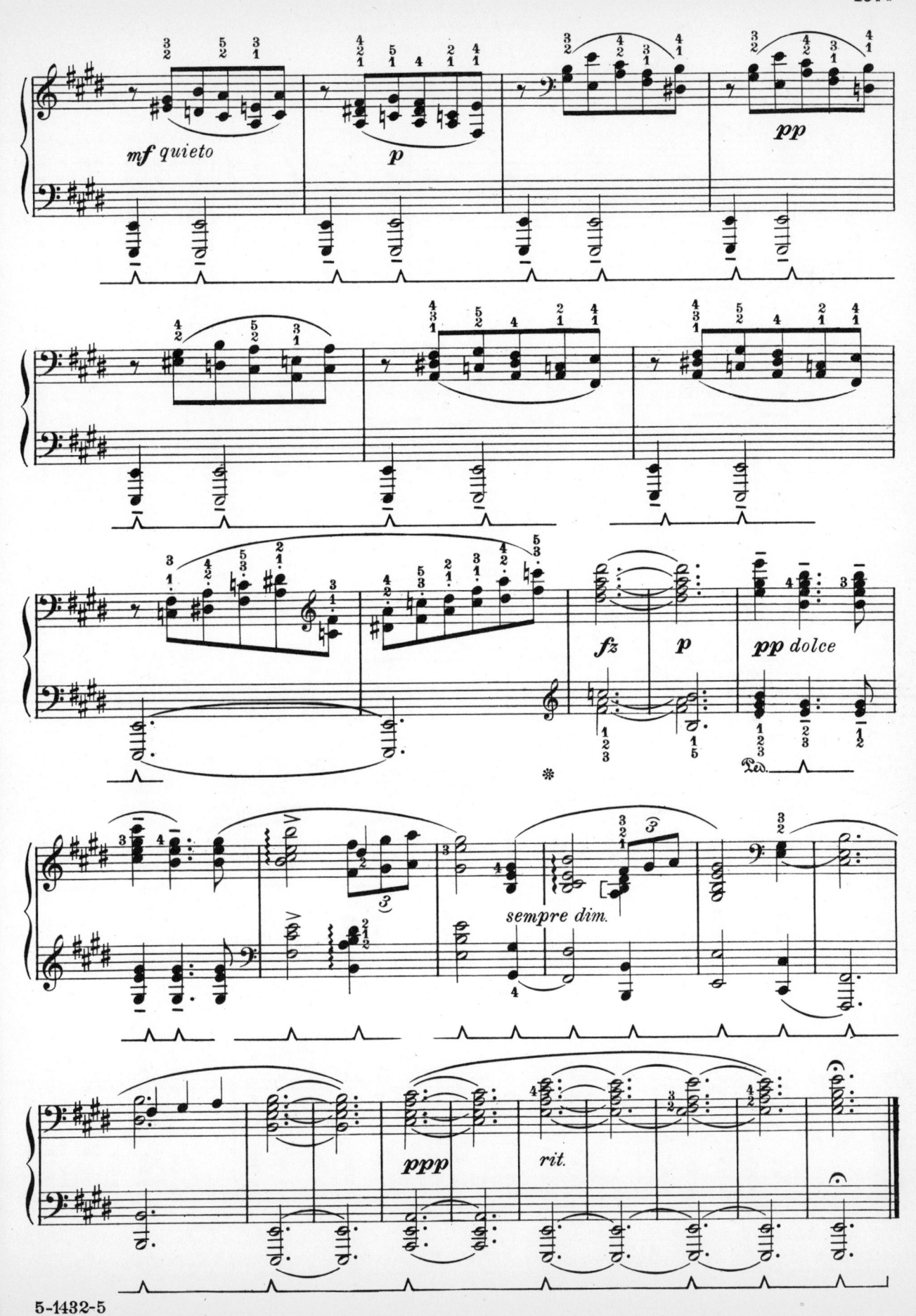

PRÉLUDE
A-FLAT MAJOR

From the Century Library of Music
Edited by Ignace J. Paderewski

Fr. CHOPIN
Op. 28, No 17

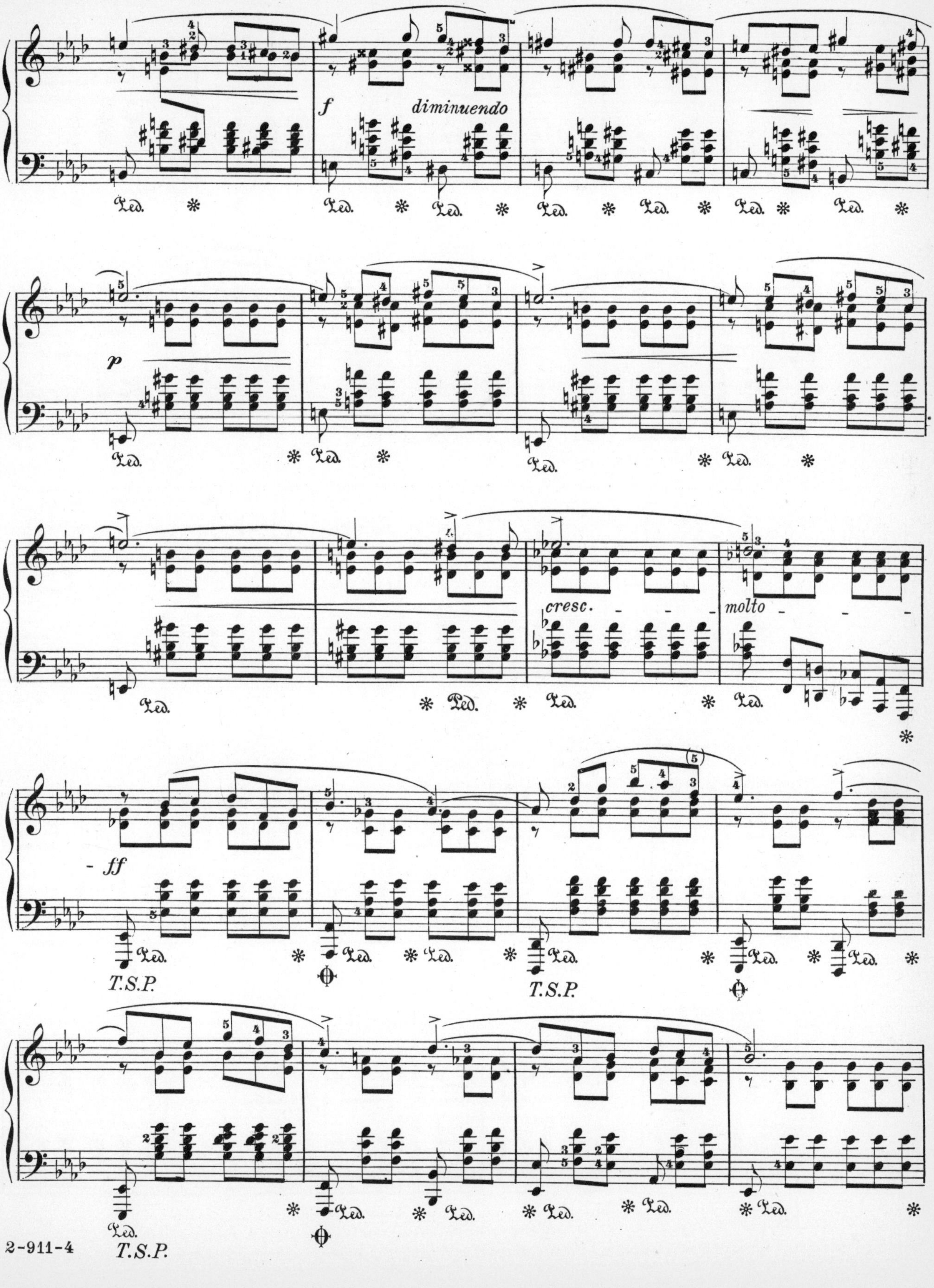

T.S.P.

1580

1581

PRELUDE
C-SHARP MINOR
(For the left hand alone)

Edited by Rudolph Ganz

ALEXANDER SCRIÀBINE, Op. 9, No. 1.

1583

TANGO BURLESCO

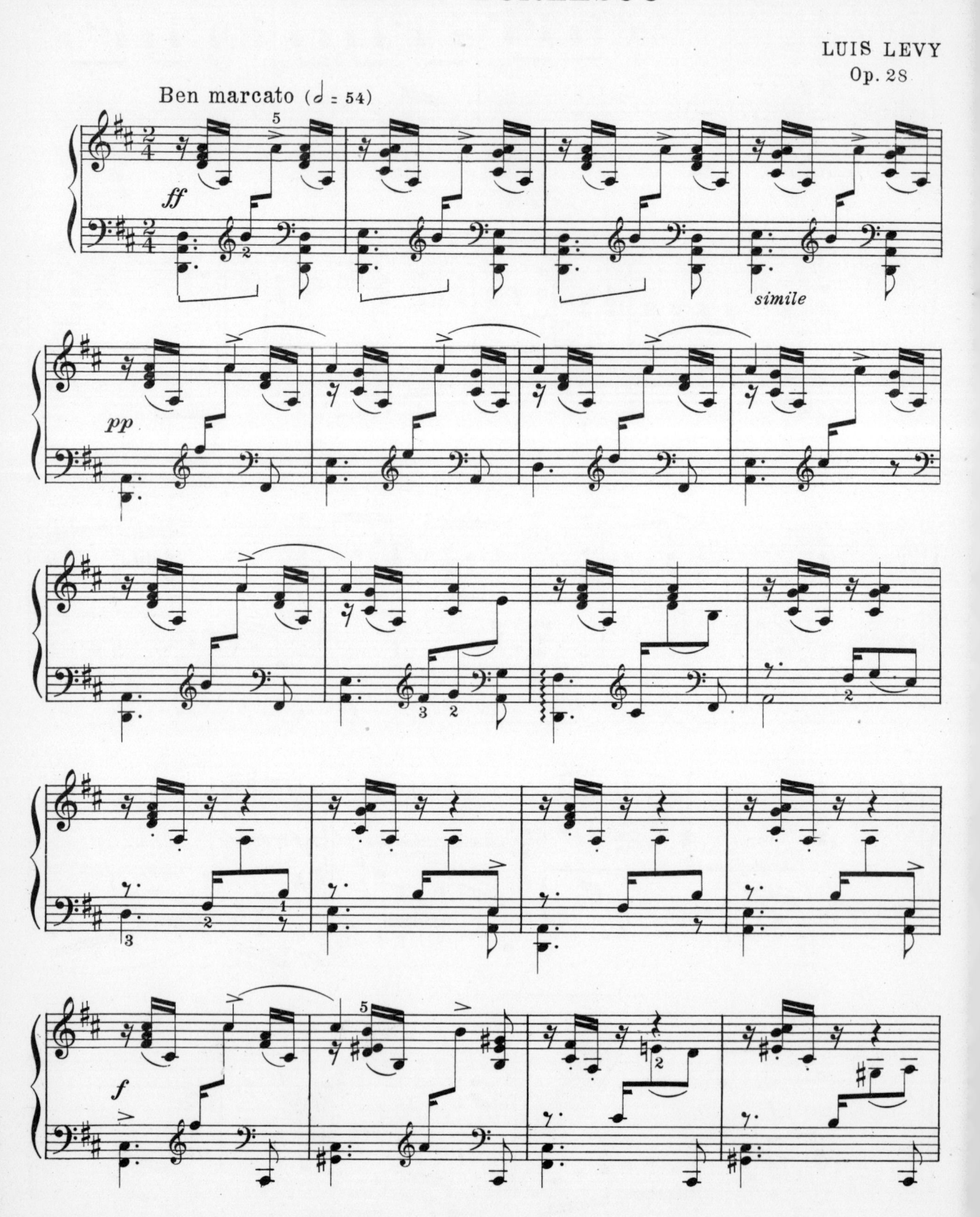

LUIS LEVY
Op. 28

Ben marcato (♩ = 54)

1585

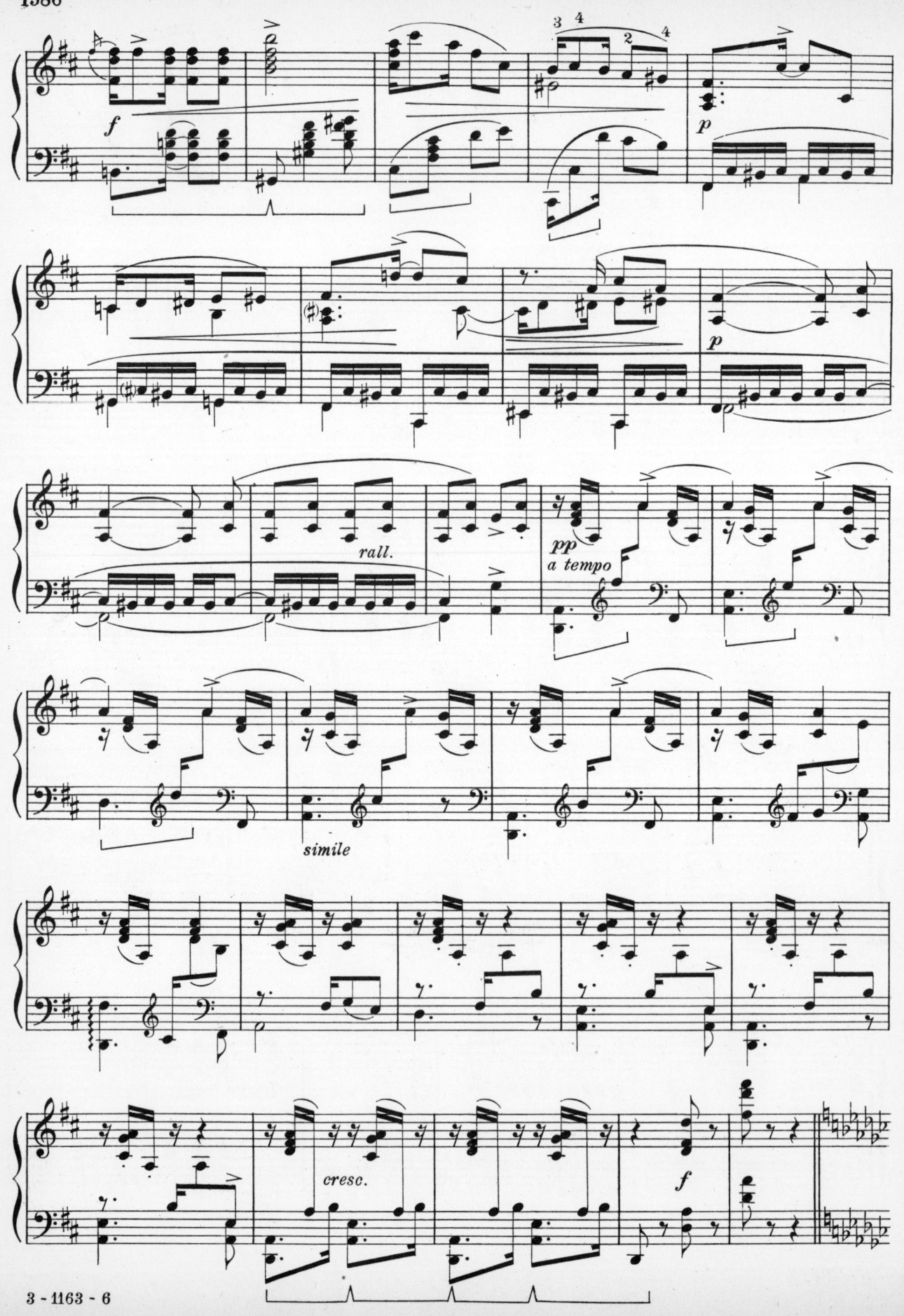

f
p
p
rall.
pp
a tempo
simile
cresc.
f

Meno mosso (𝅗𝅥 = 50)

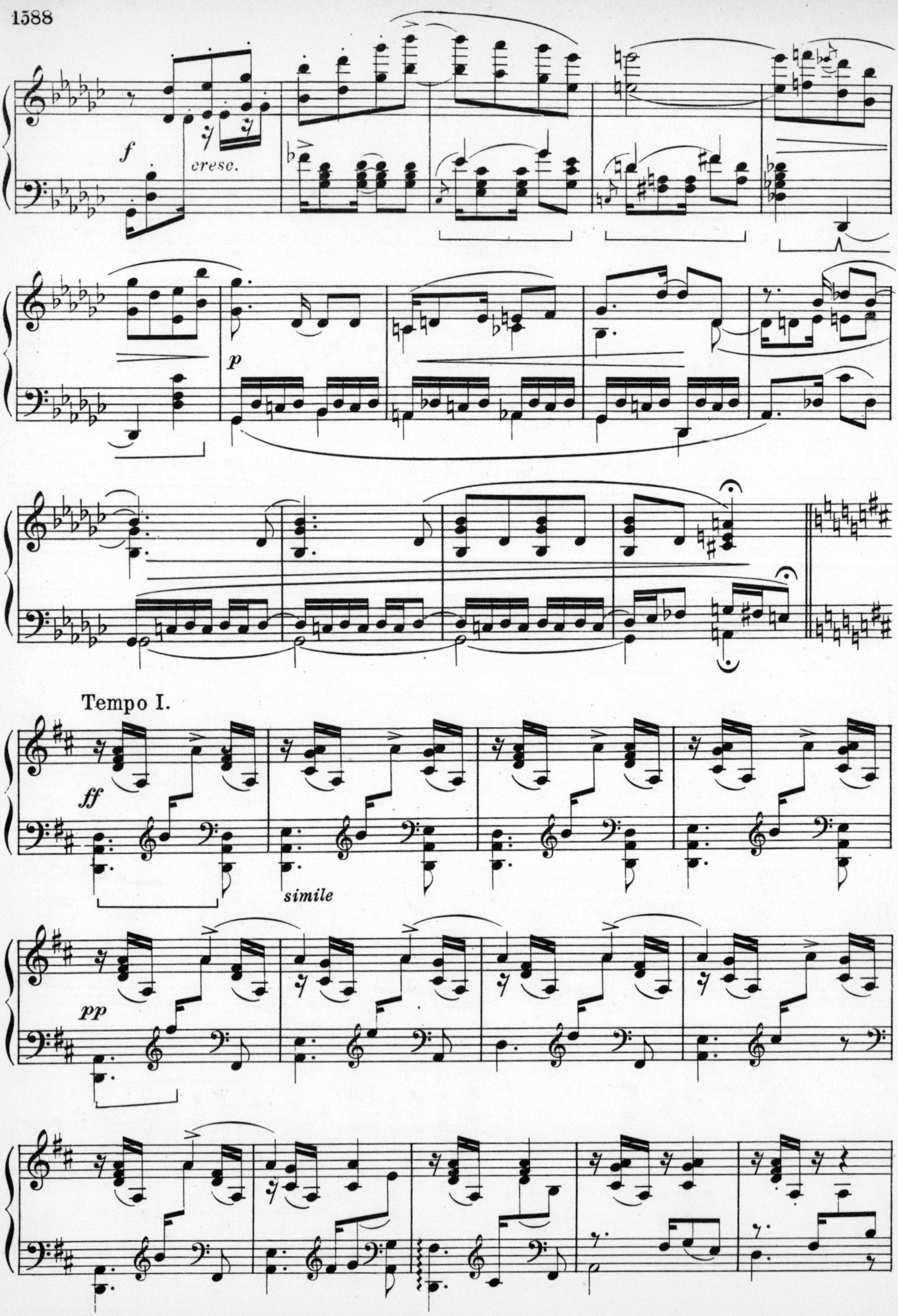
f
cresc.
p
Tempo I.
ff
simile
pp

1589

CAPRICE

Edited by
Nicholas de Vore

MAX REGER
Op. 79a, No. 4b.

Estremamente vivo

1591

CAPRICE
G MAJOR

Edited by Vernon Spencer

ARENSKY Op. 43, No. 4

Allegro

1593

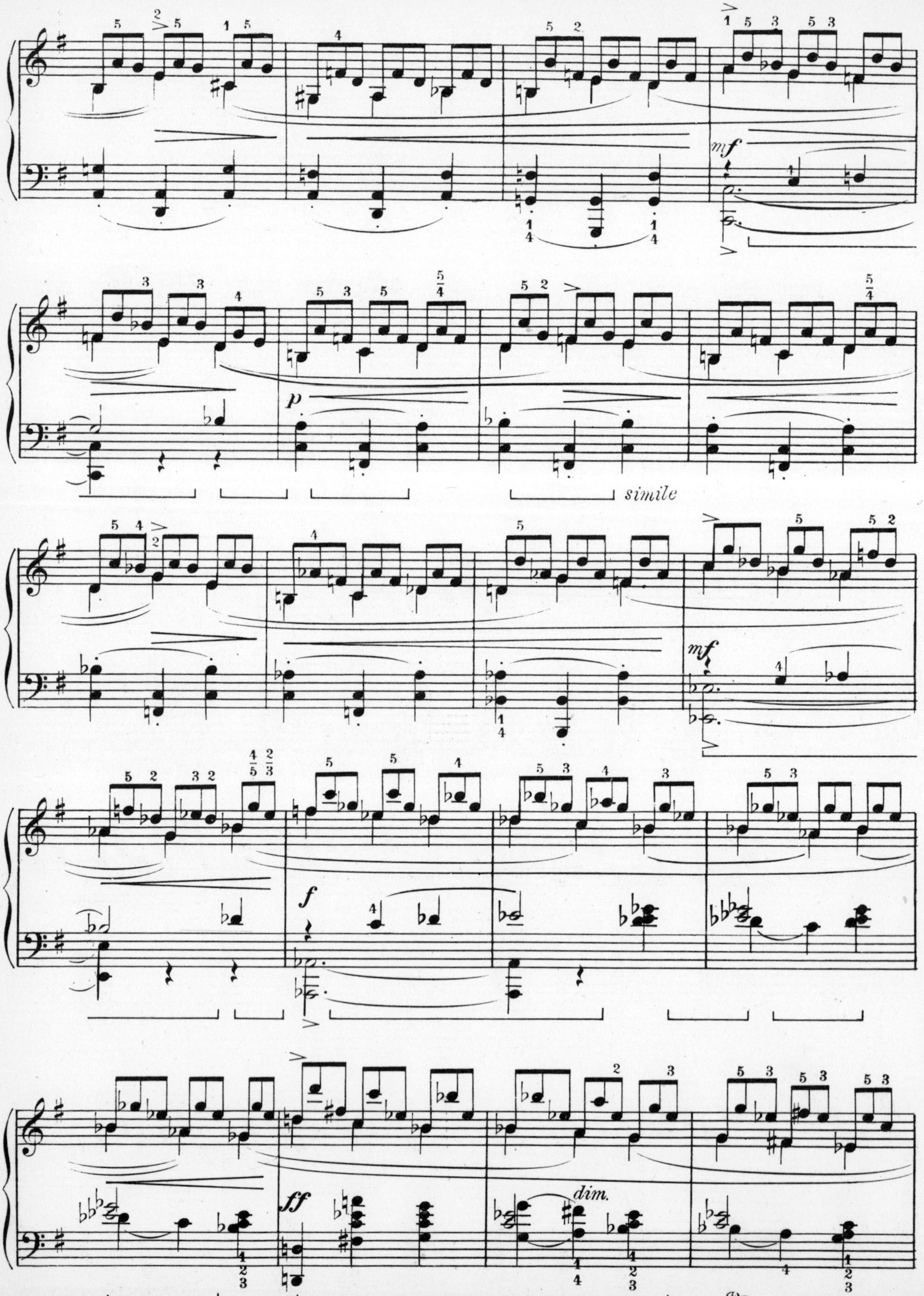
mf
p
simile
mf
f
ff
dim.
senza Ped.

1595

ARABESQUE
IN FORM OF AN ETUDE

Edited by
Charles Dennée

TH. LESCHETIZKY
Op. 45, No. 1

Allegretto con moto

1597

1598

1599

RONDO CAPRICCIOSO

Edited by August Fraemcke

F. MENDELSSOHN
Op. 14

1601

1602

1603

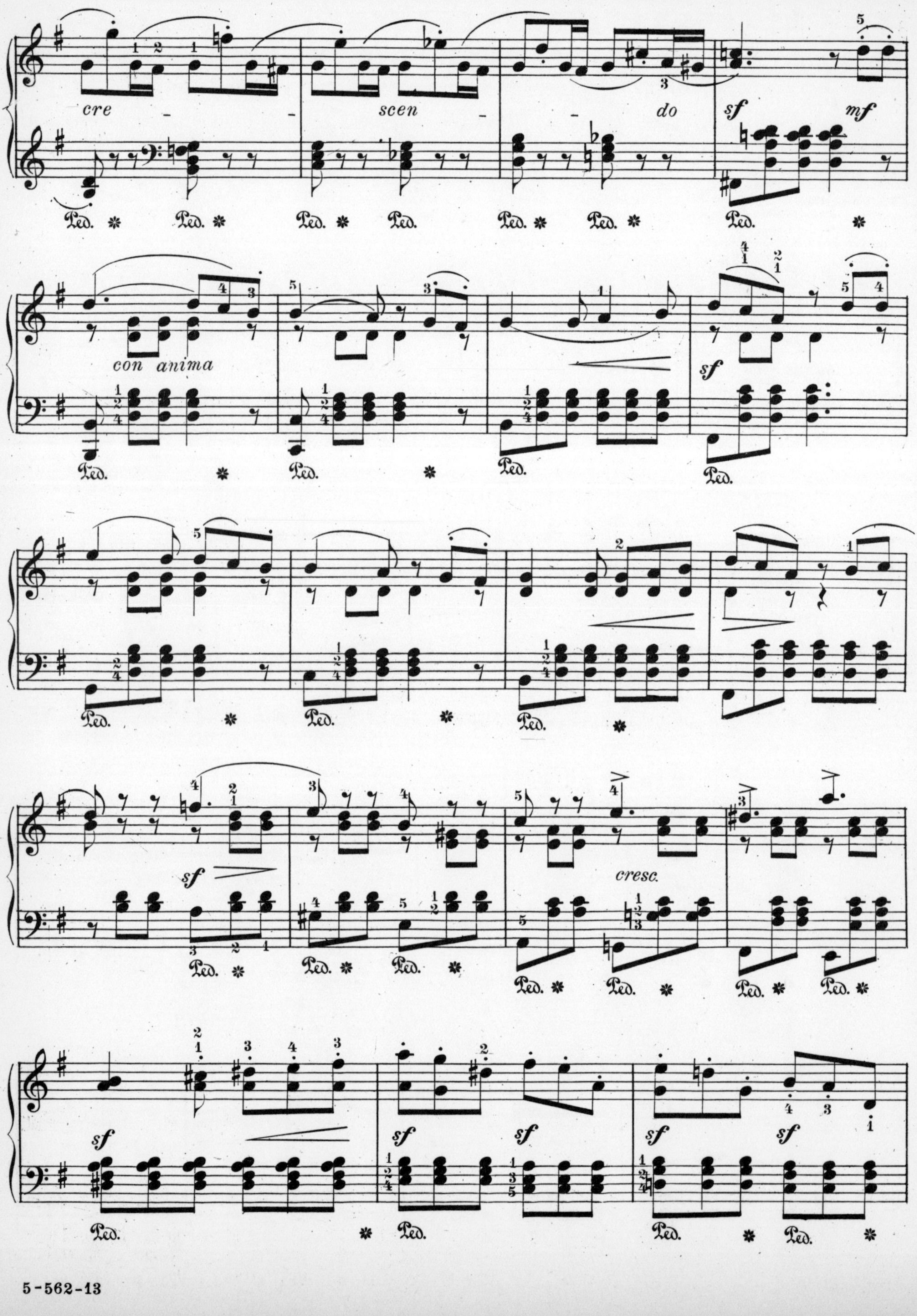
cre - scen - do
sf
mf
con anima
sf
sf
cresc.
sf
sf
sf
sf
sf

1605

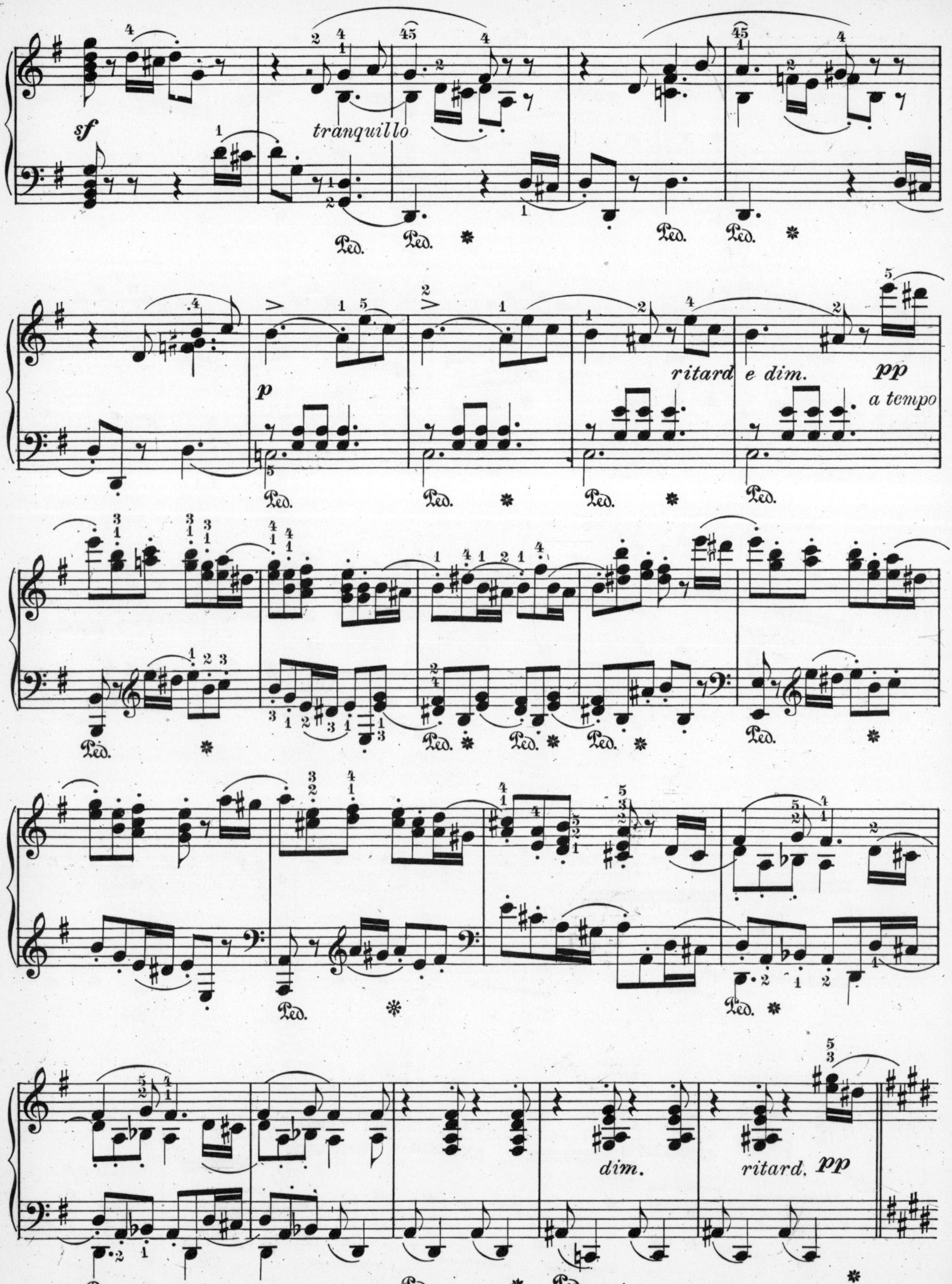
sf
tranquillo
Ped.
p
ritard e dim.
pp
a tempo
dim.
ritard.
pp

1607

1608

1609

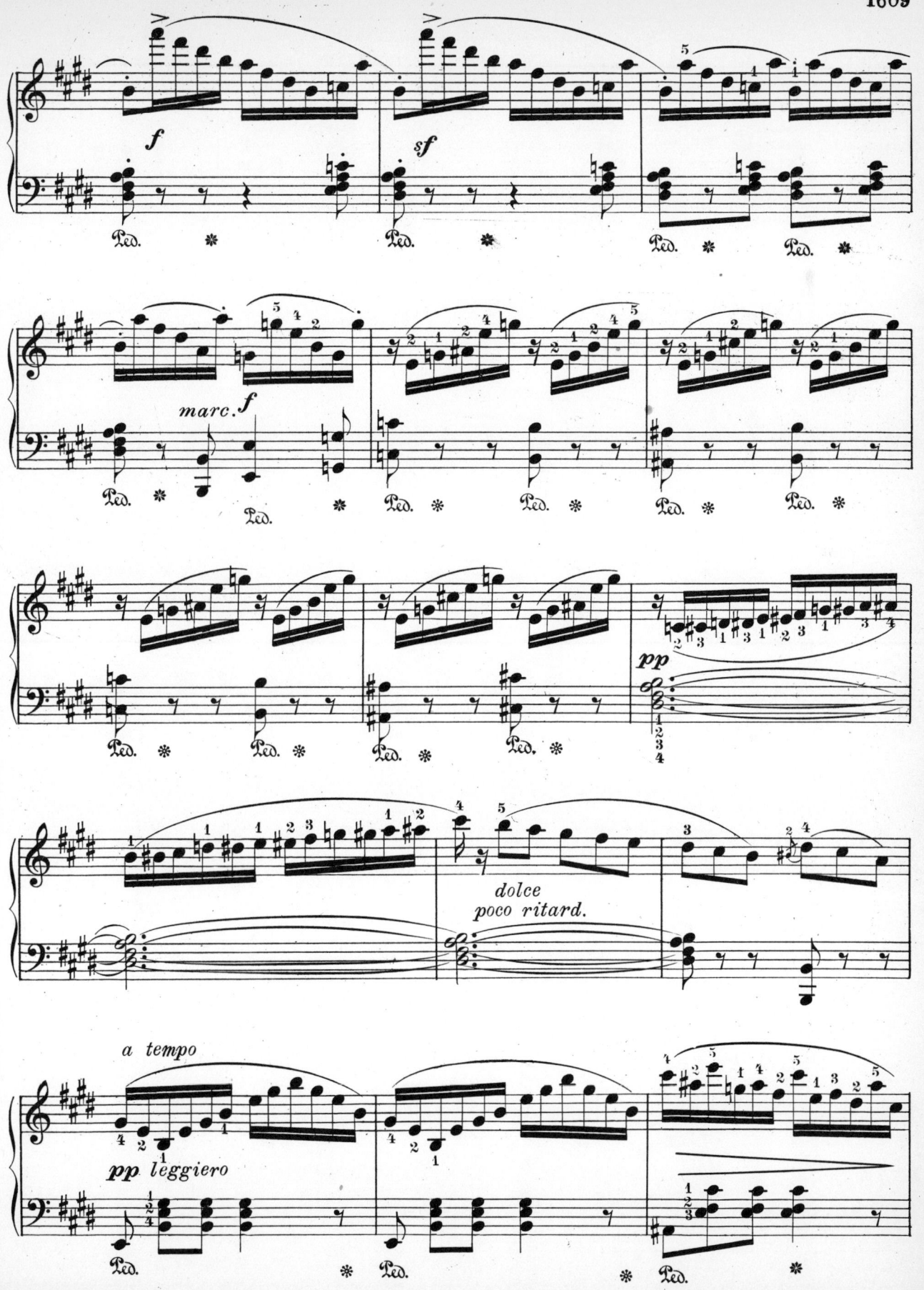

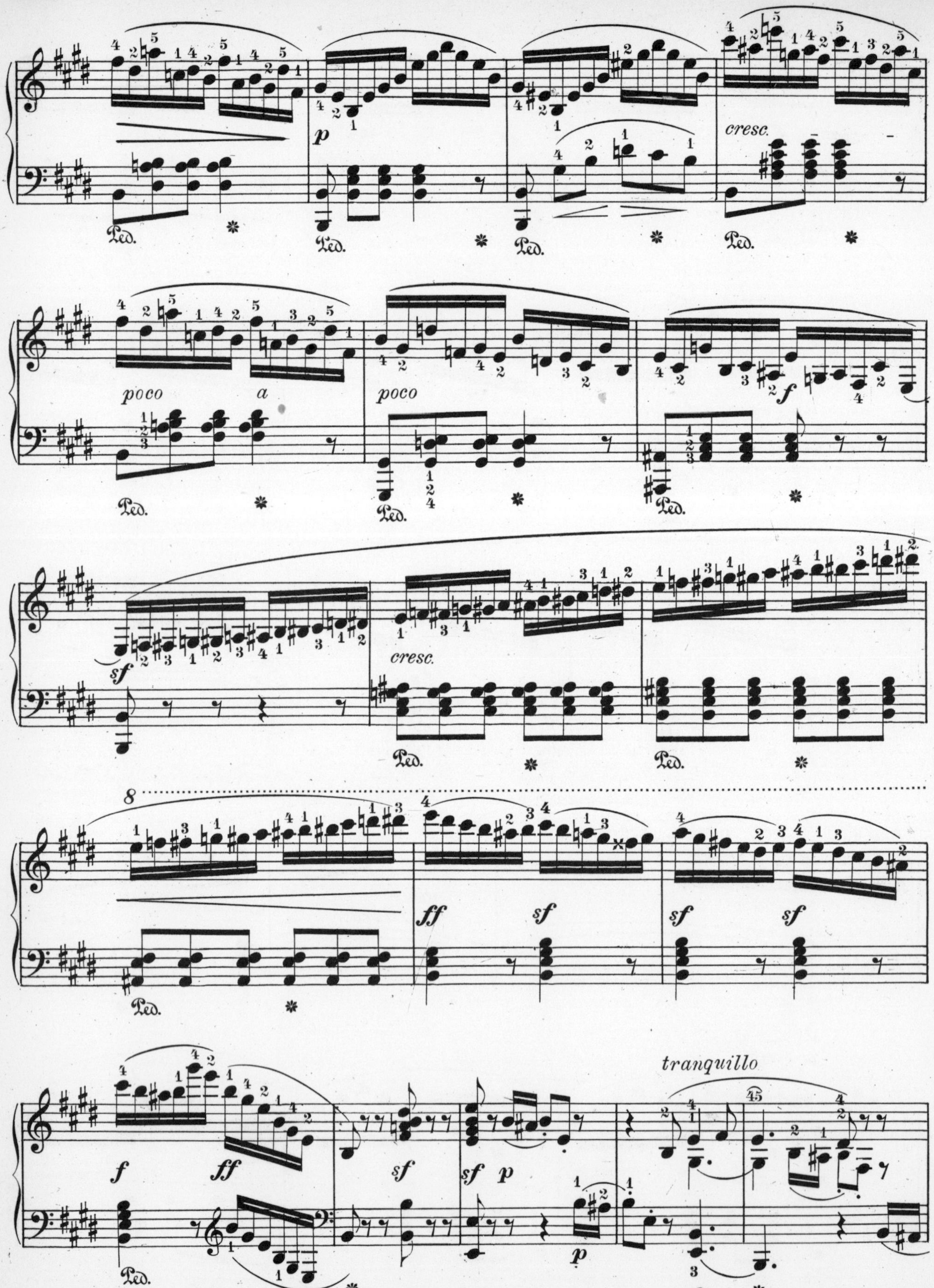
cresc.
poco
a
poco
cresc.
tranquillo
Ped.

1611

Ped. * Ped. * Ped. * Ped. * Ped. *
dim.
a tempo
pp poco ritard.
ff
poco a poco strin-gen-do.
ff
Ped. * Ped. * Ped. * Ped. * Ped. * Ped. * Ped. *

WALTZES
WALZER

Edited by Rudolph Ganz

J. BRAHMS
Op. 39
(*Abridged*)

Grazioso
II.
p espressivo
poco cresc.
Ped. simile
p
p
poco cresc.
simile
p
p
dim. e rit.
1.
2.

Andante espressivo

Moderato
IV.
p dolce
sotto voce
simile
simile
simile
sosten.
simile
pp semplice
1.
2.

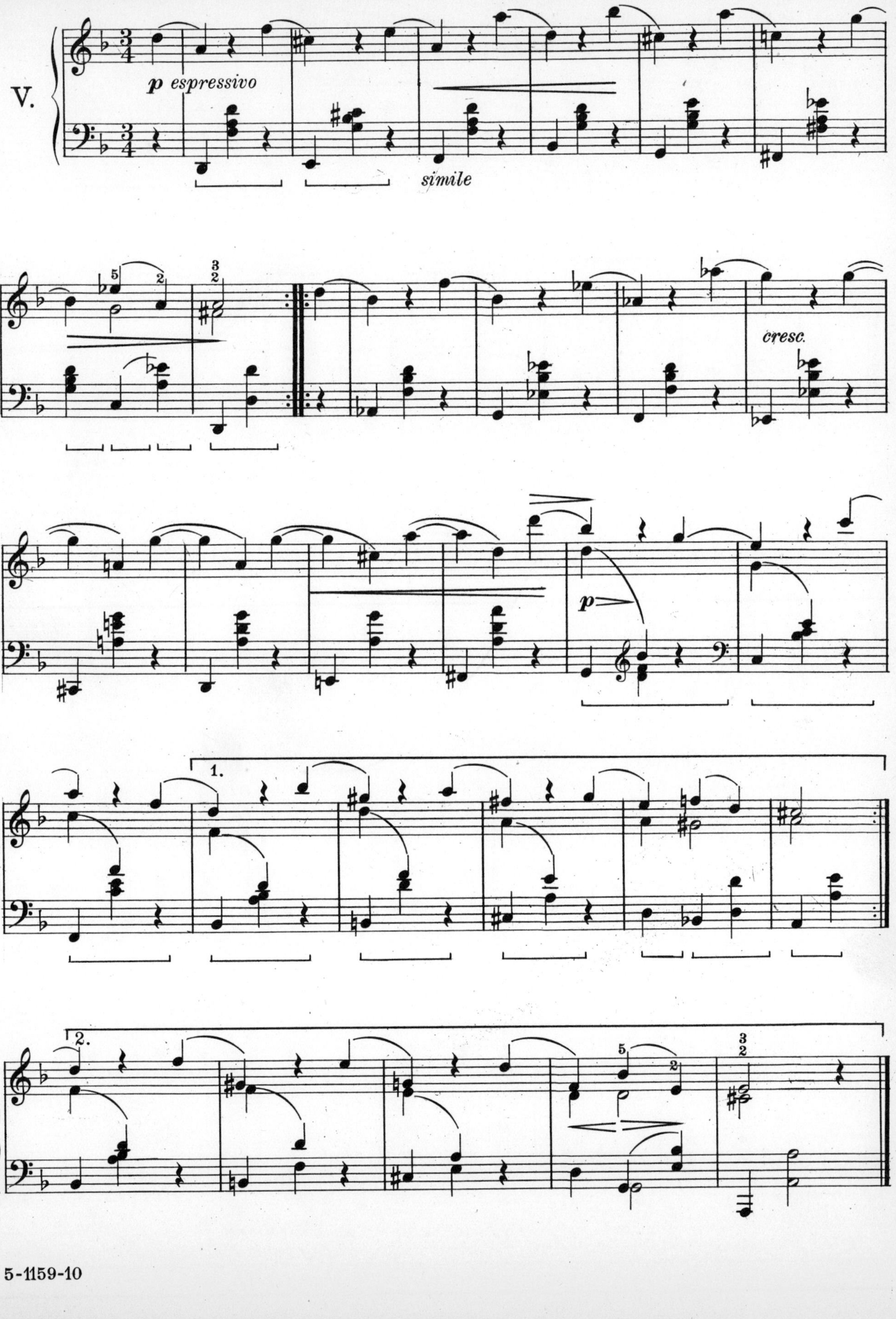
V.
p espressivo
simile
cresc.
p
1.
2.

VI.
p poco scherzando
legg.
1.
2.
sempre meno
1.
2.
Alla zingara
VII.
fp
simile
p
simile

1619

Moderato
VIII.
p
dolce
simile
sosten.
1.
2.
p dolce
legato
simile
espr.
mf
p
simile
1.
2.

IX.

X. Moderato assai

BARCAROLE

G MAJOR, № IV

From the CENTURY LIBRARY of MUSIC
Edited by Ignace J. Paderewski
Allegretto con moto

A. RUBINSTEIN

ben marcato la melodia
l'accompagnamento pp e con pedale
l.h.
r.h.
mf
sf
p

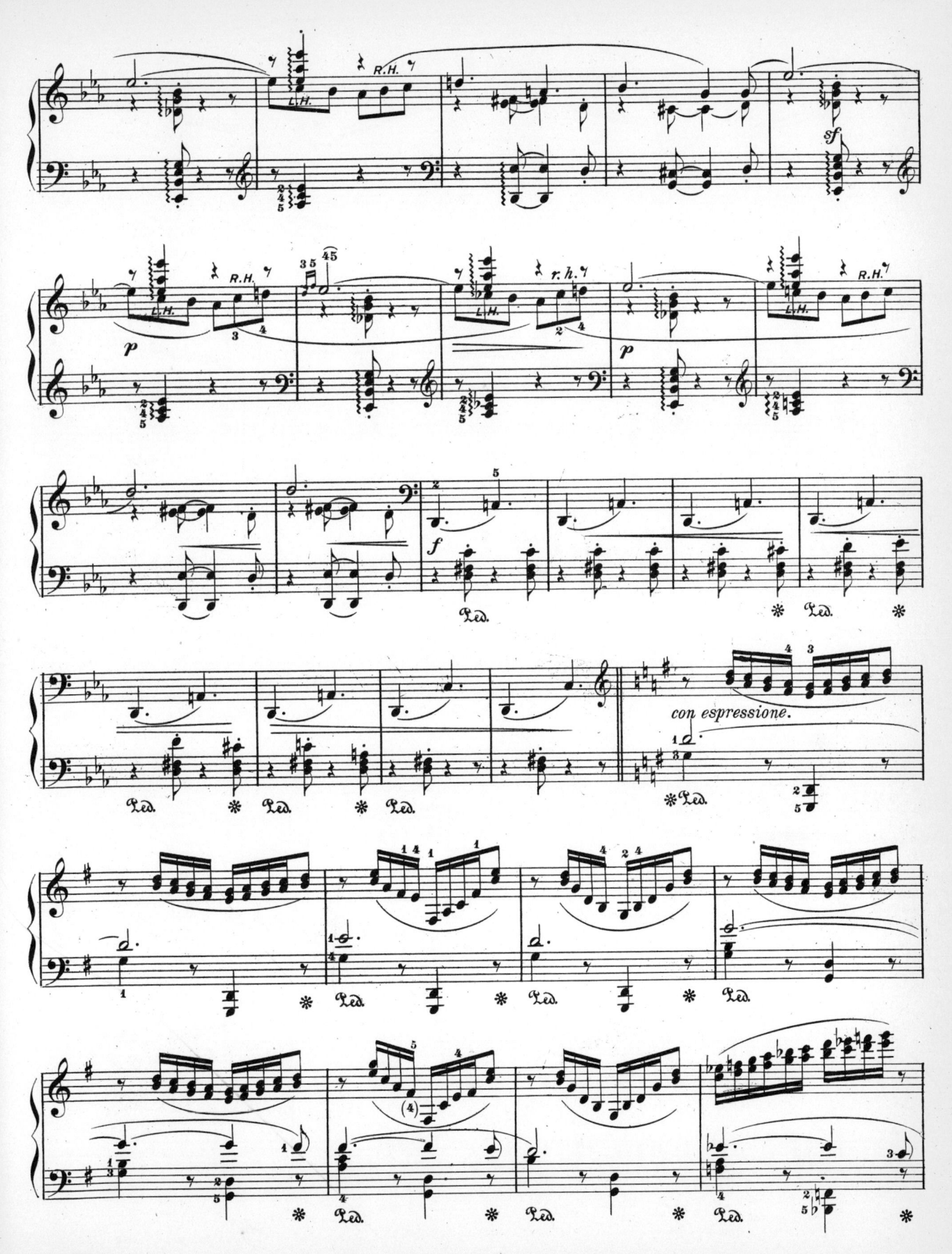
R.H.
L.H.
sf
p
r. h.
f
Ped.
con espressione.

1626

1627

BARCAROLLE
F MINOR

From the CENTURY LIBRARY of MUSIC
Edited by Ignace J. Paderewski

A. RUBINSTEIN
Op. 30, No. 1

Moderato assai

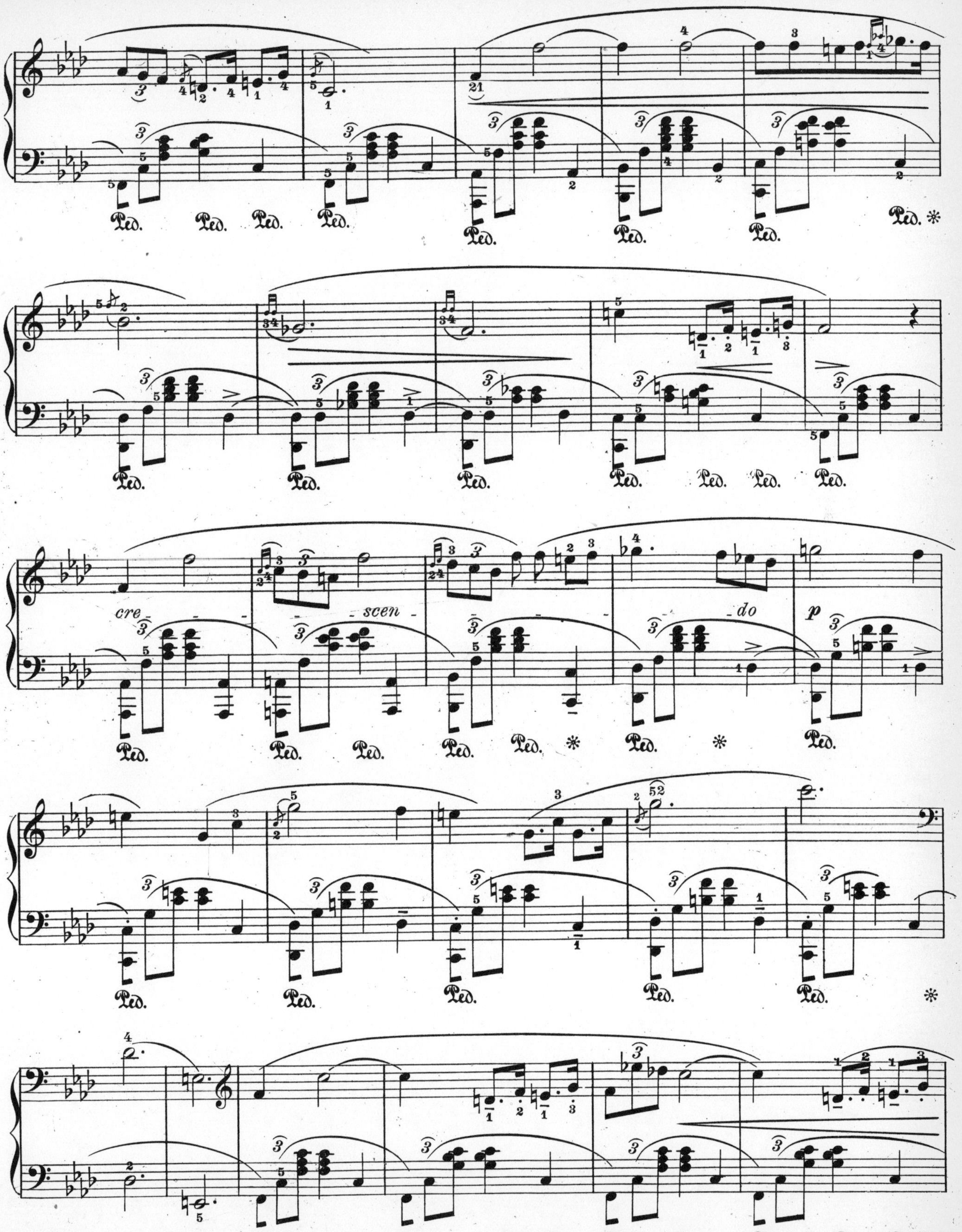
Ped.
cre
scen
do
p
Ped.

1630

1631

1632

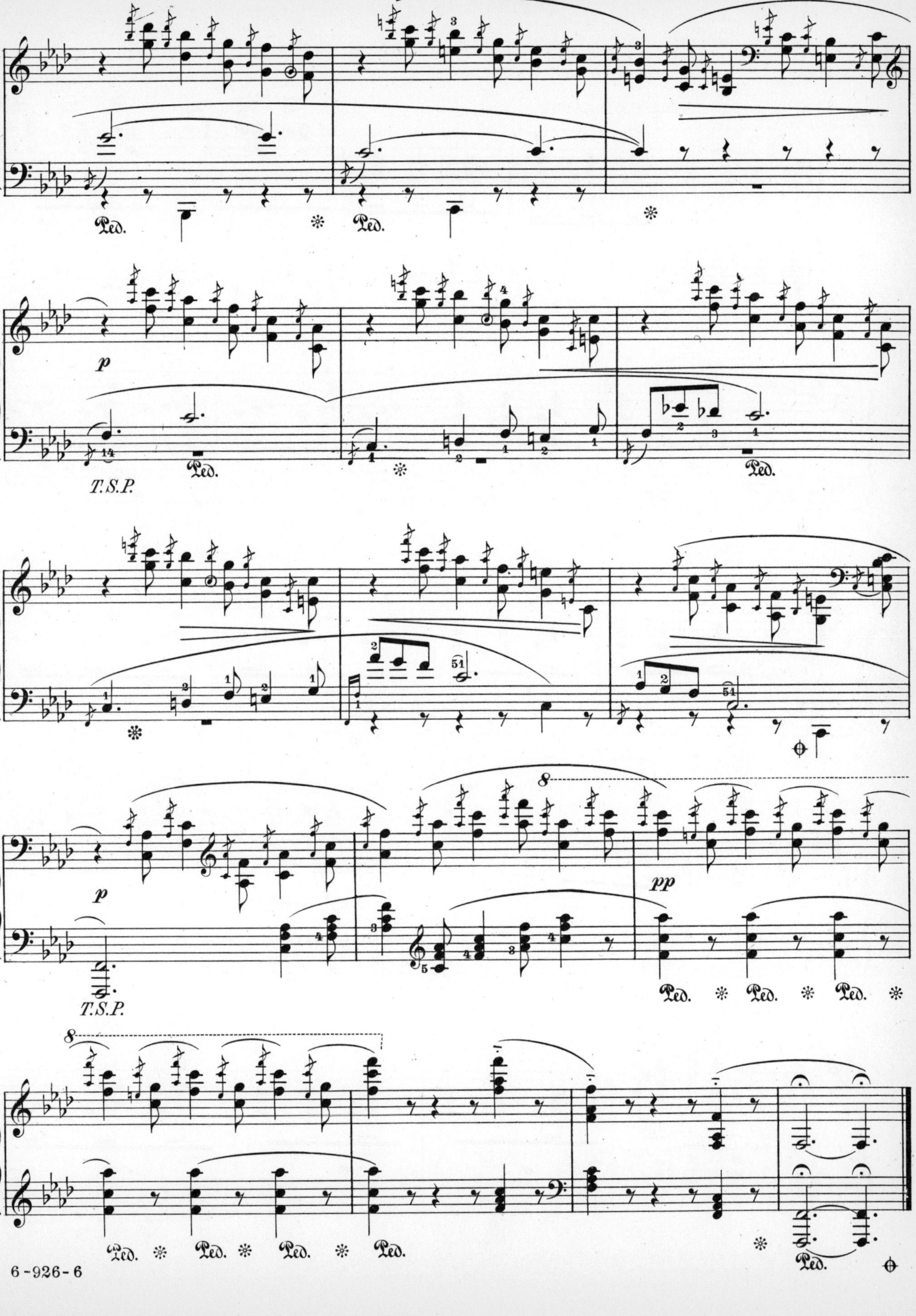

Ped.
p
T.S.P.
pp

SEGUIDILLA
CASTILIAN DANCE

Edited by A. Pero

I. ALBENIZ

Allegro e leggiero

un poco marcato il basso

1635

animato
p
cresc.
f
p
cresc.
8
f
ff
L'istesso tempo
pp
f
p
p
f
cresc.
rit. molto
f
a tempo

1637

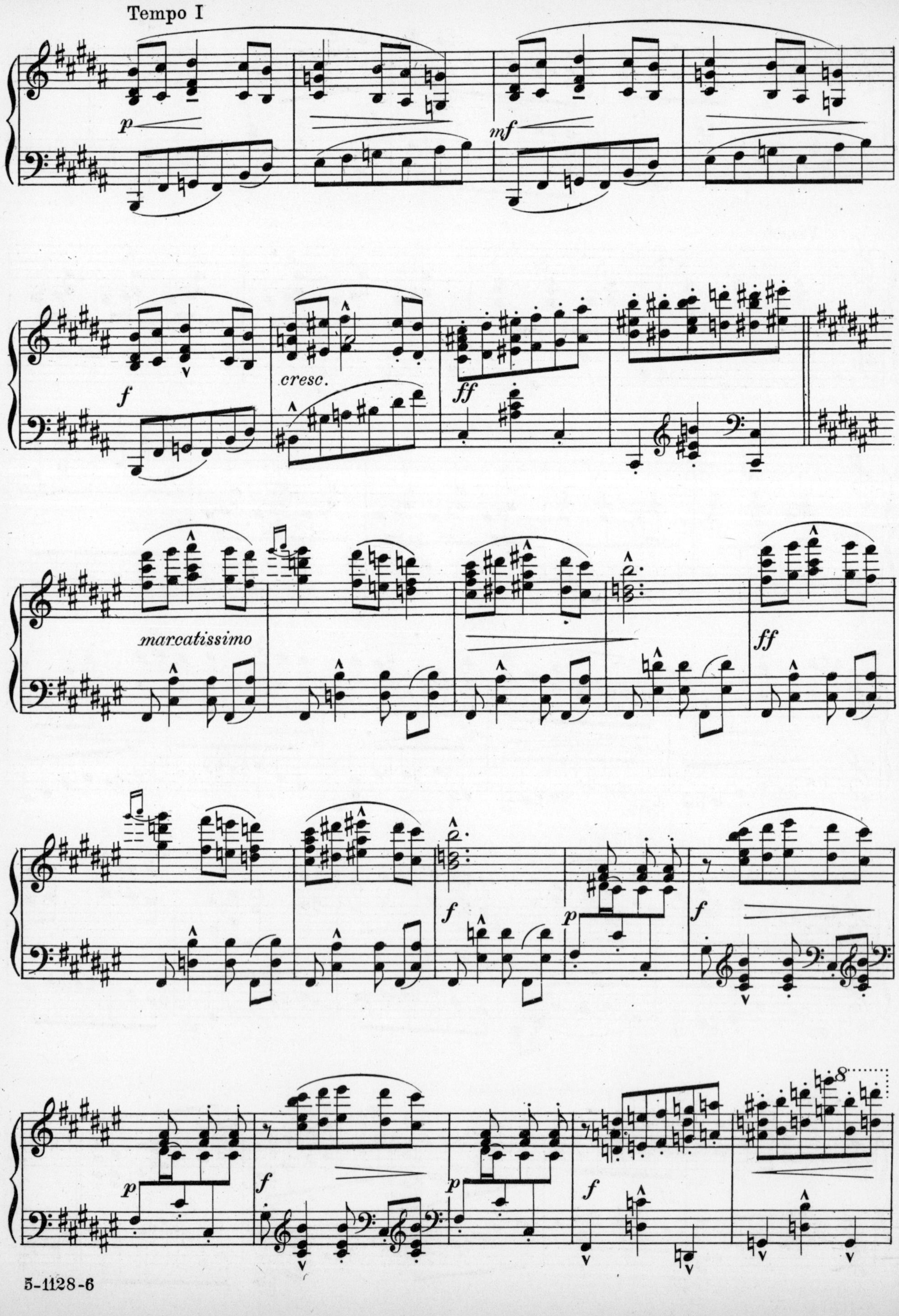
Tempo I
p
mf
f
cresc.
ff
marcatissimo
ff
f
p
f
p
f
p
f
8

1639

WITCHES' DANCE
HEXENTANZ

E. A. MAC DOWELL
Op. 17, N.º 2

Presto (♩.=126)

1641

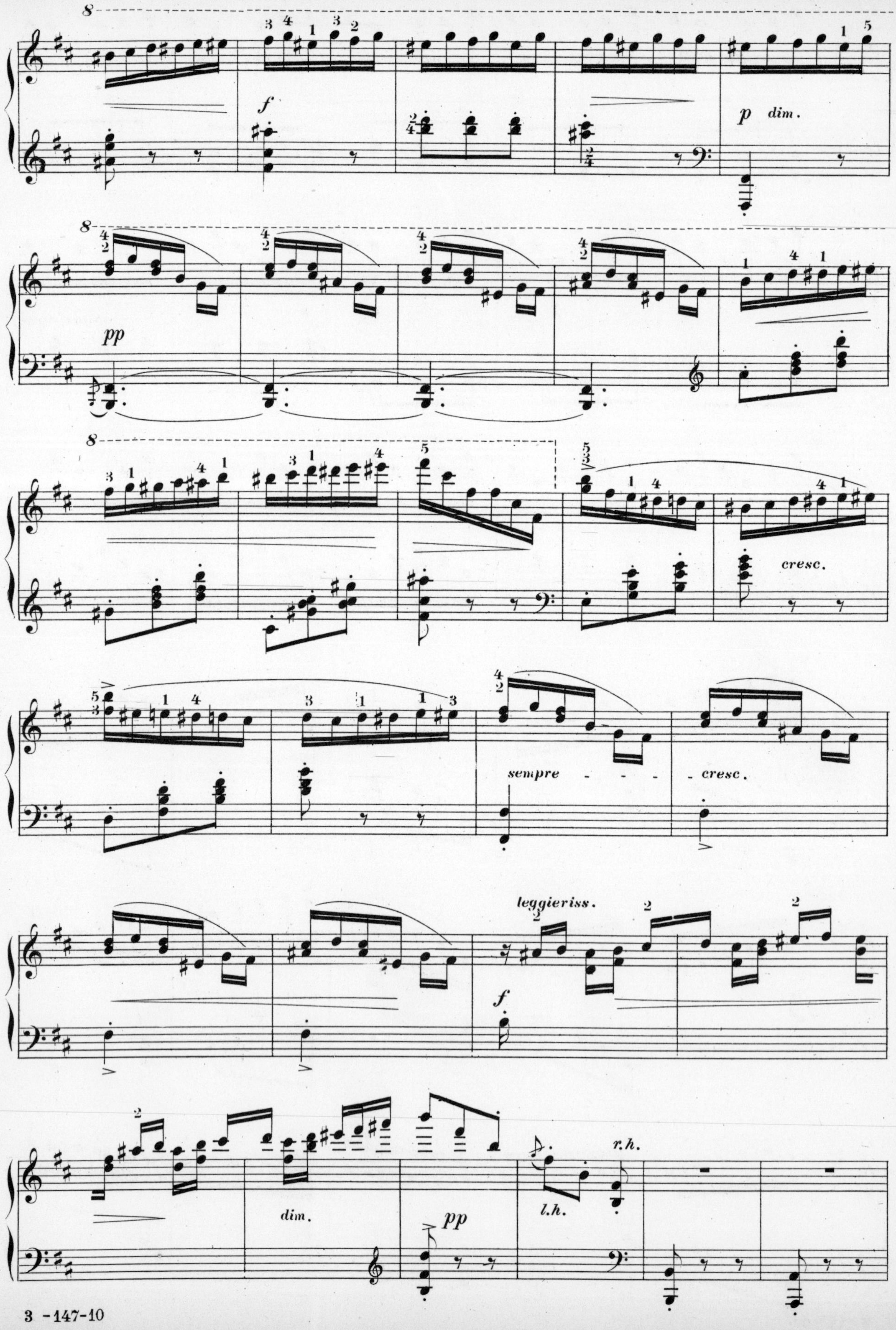
f
p dim.
pp
cresc.
sempre - - - - cresc.
leggieriss.
f
dim.
pp
r.h.
l.h.

1643

a tempo.
poco rall.
ff e marcatiss.
8
8
ff
staccatiss
leggiero
8
f
ff
martellato

pp dolce
leggiero e non legato
sempre
poco a poco
a tempo
rall.
dolciss
molto
rall.
legg.
p
f
p
3
8
f
f

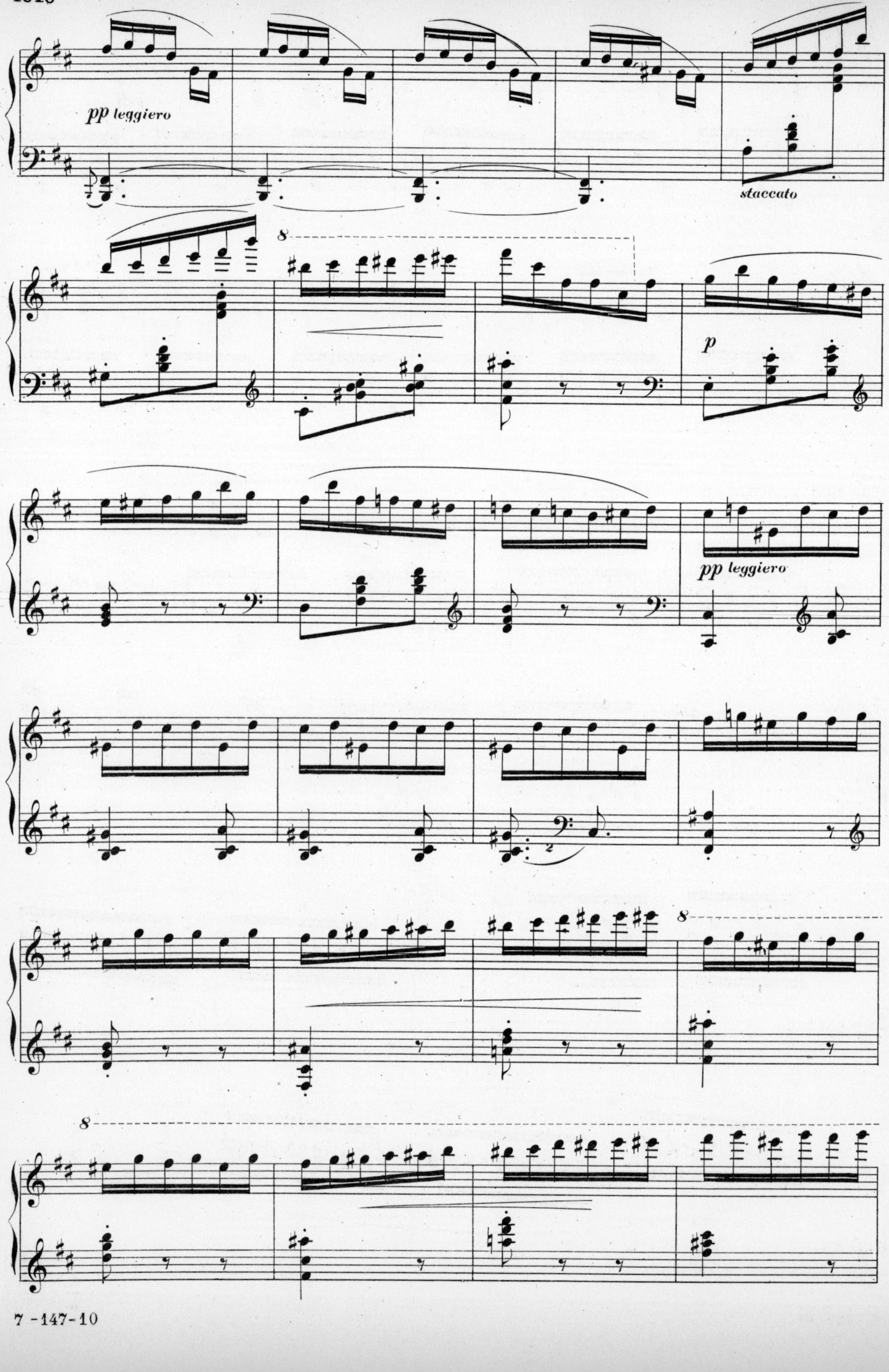
pp leggiero
staccato
8
p
pp leggiero
8
8

1647

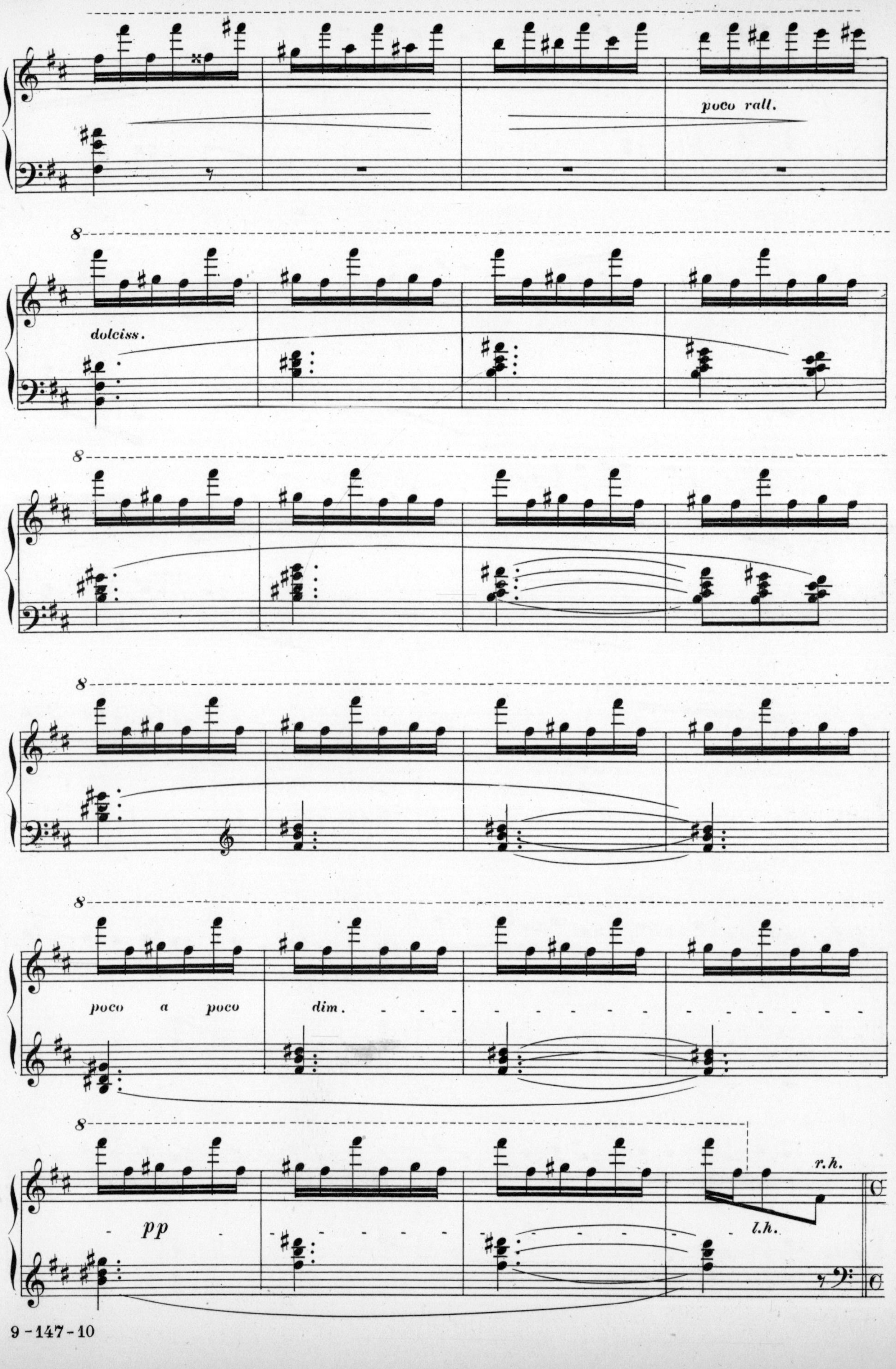
poco rall.
8
dolciss.
8
8
8
poco a poco dim.
8
pp
r.h.
l.h.

1649

PRELUDE
B Major

SERGEI RACHMANINOFF
Op. 32, No. 11

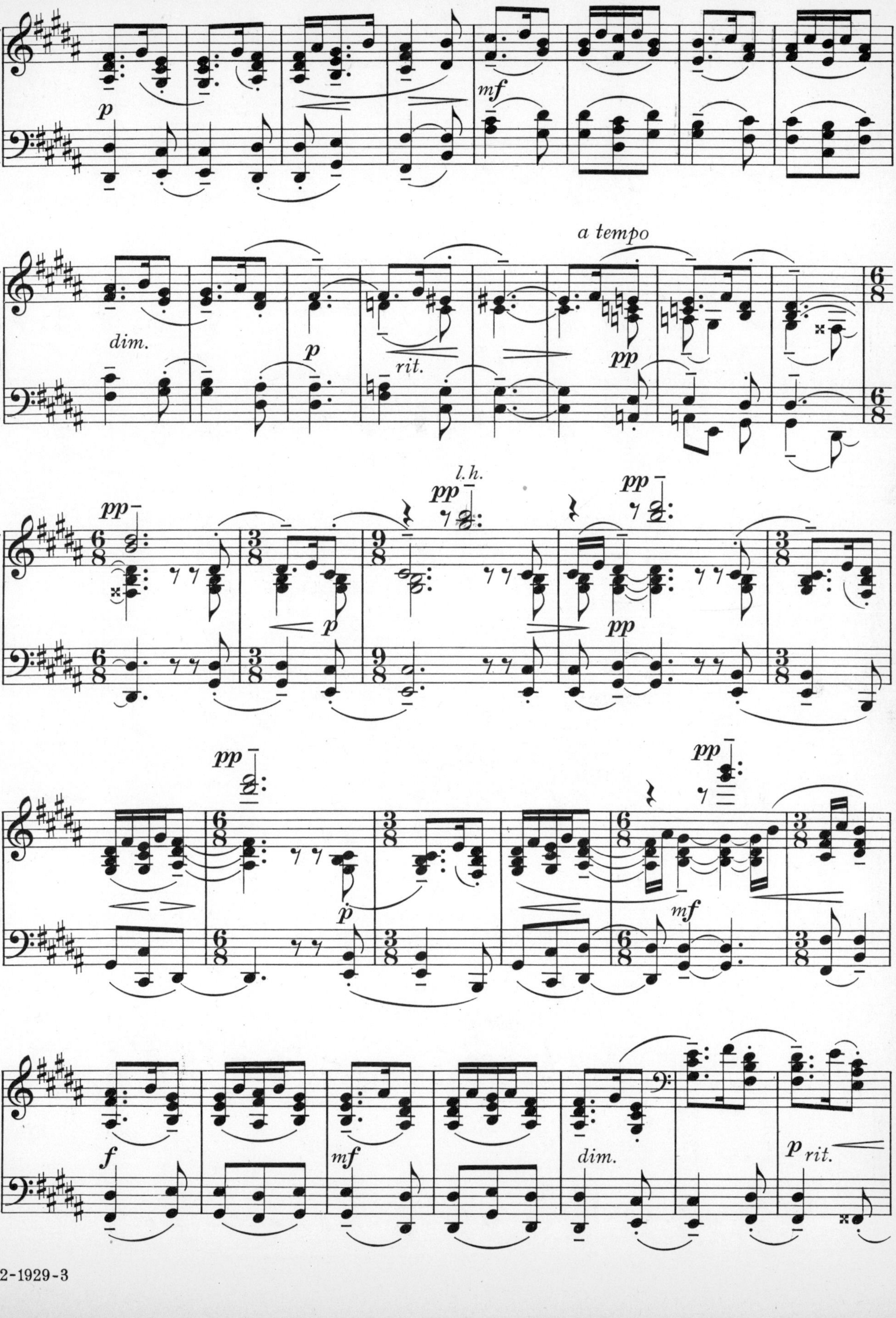
p
mf
dim.
p
rit.
a tempo
pp
pp
l.h.
pp
p
pp
pp
pp
mf
f
mf
dim.
p rit.

1652

HUMORESKE

Allegro vivace

SERGEI RACHMANINOFF
Op. 10, No. 5

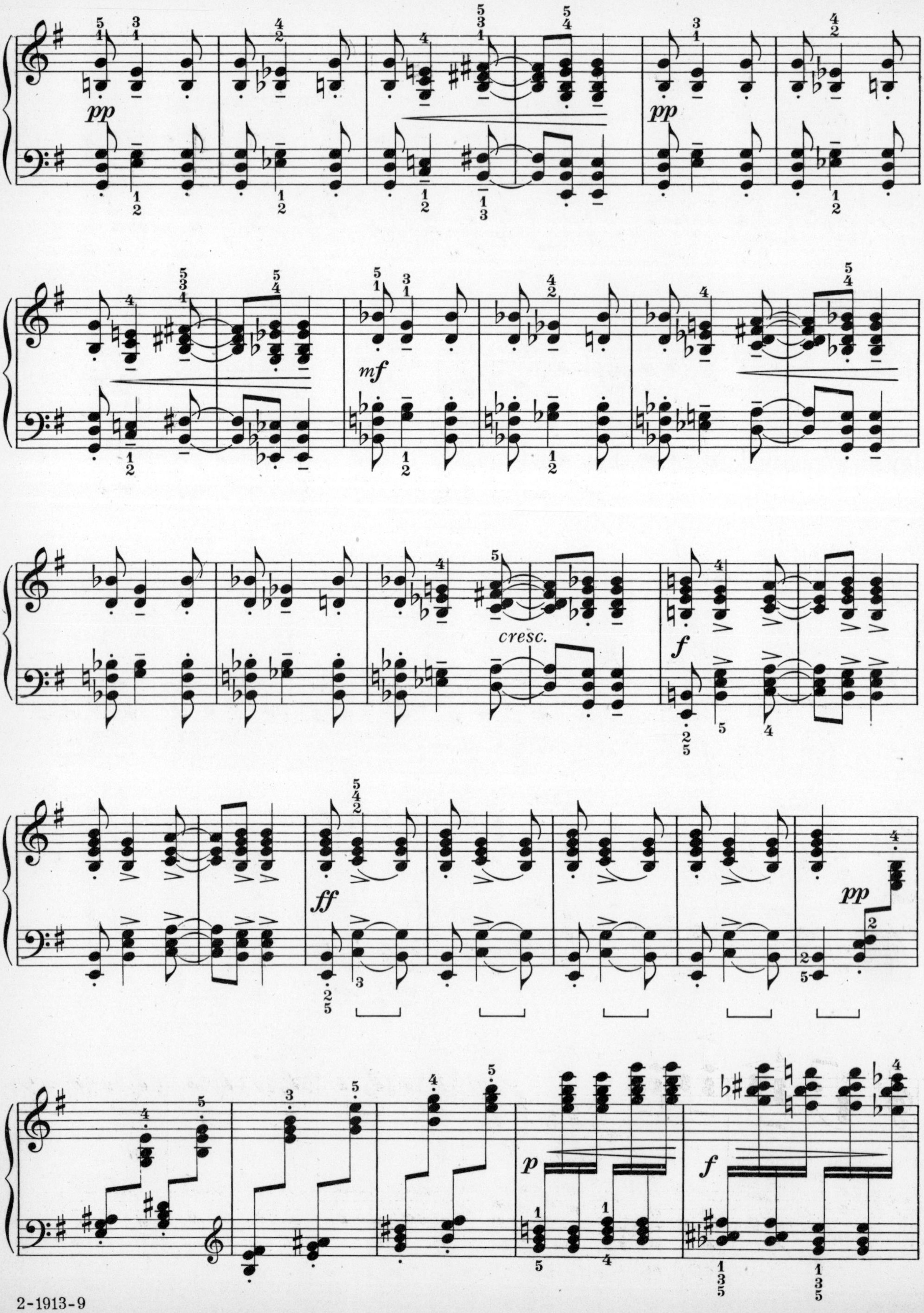
pp
pp
mf
cresc.
f
ff
pp
p
f

1655

Andante

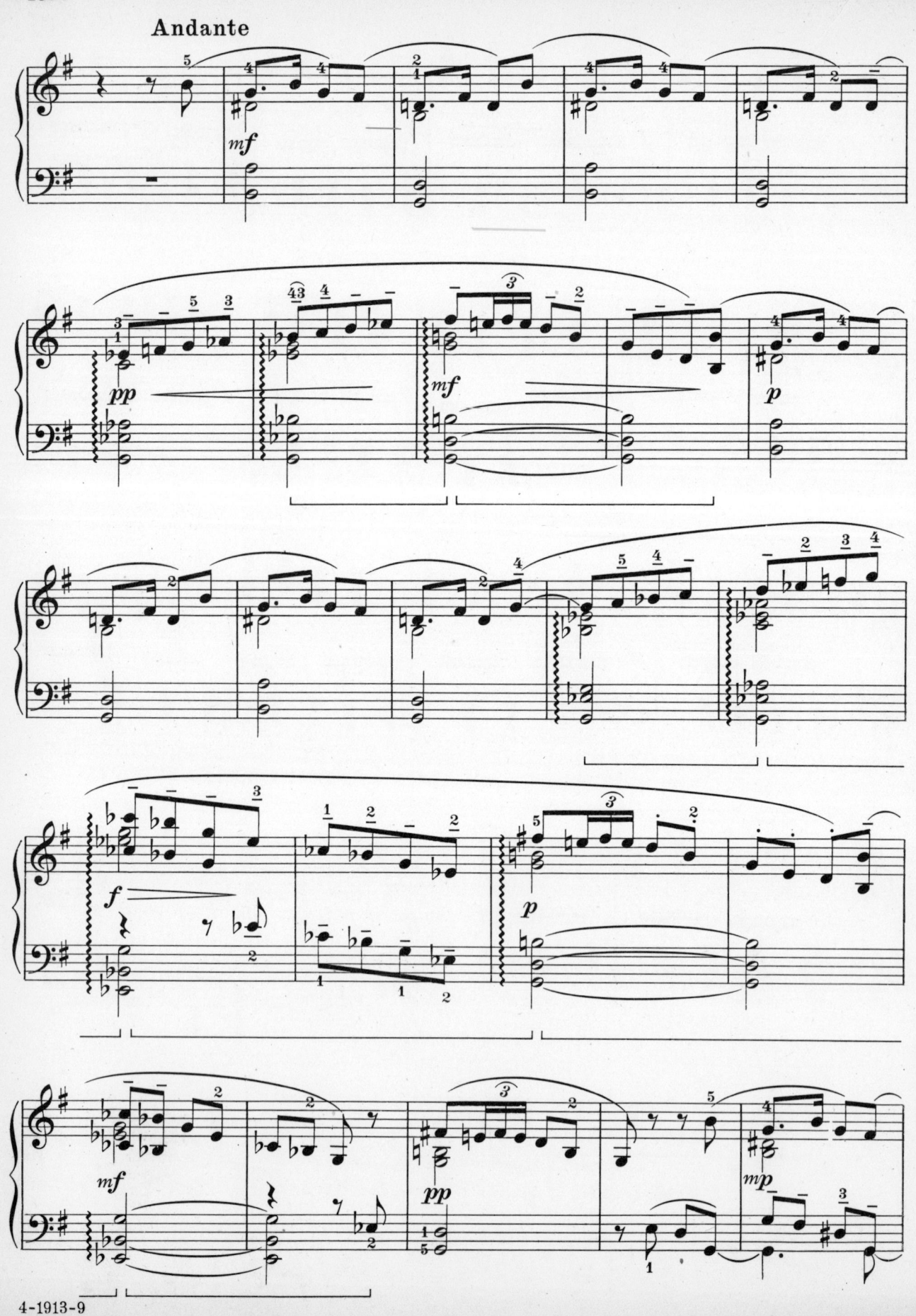

1657

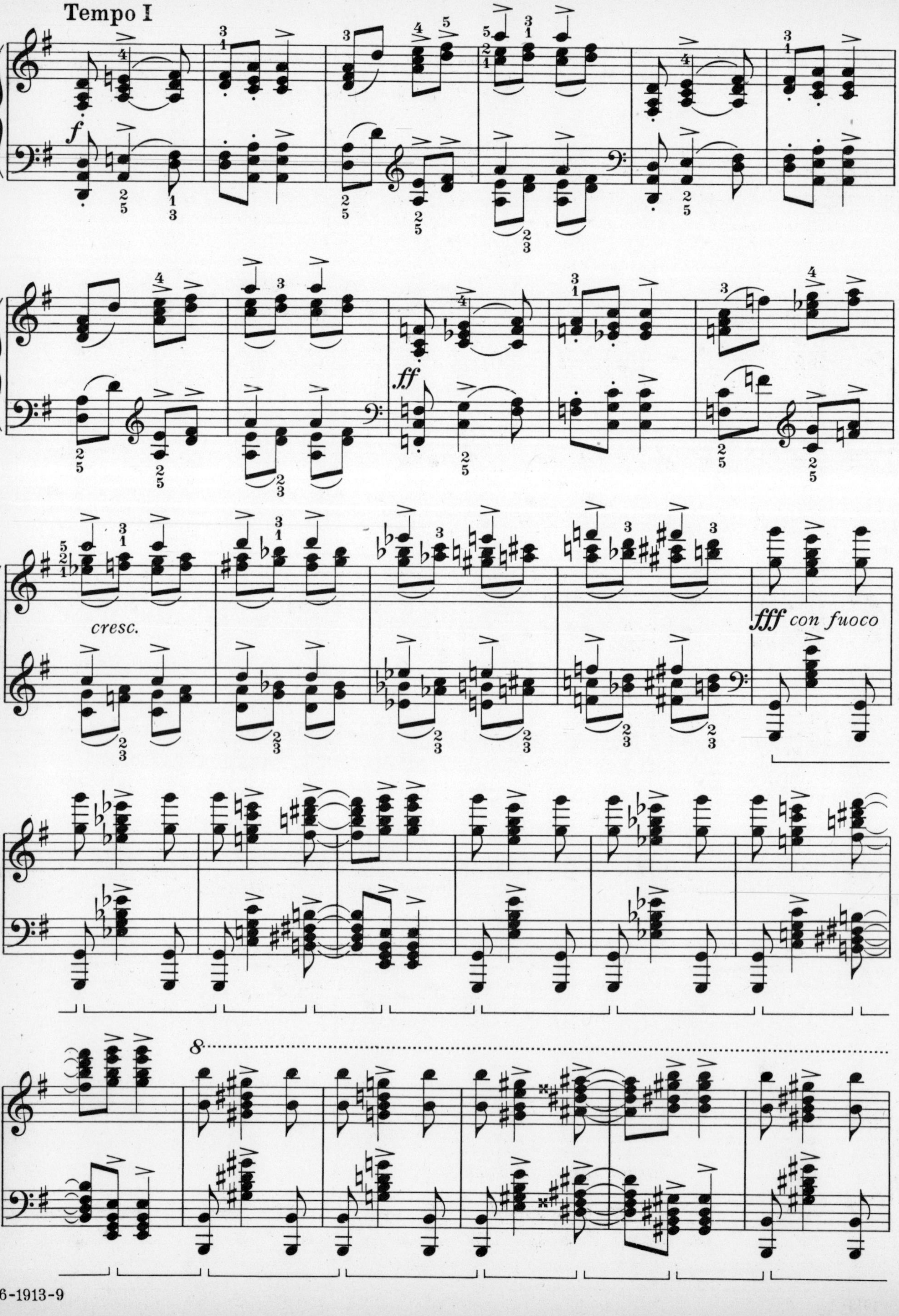
Tempo I
f
ff
cresc.
fff con fuoco
8

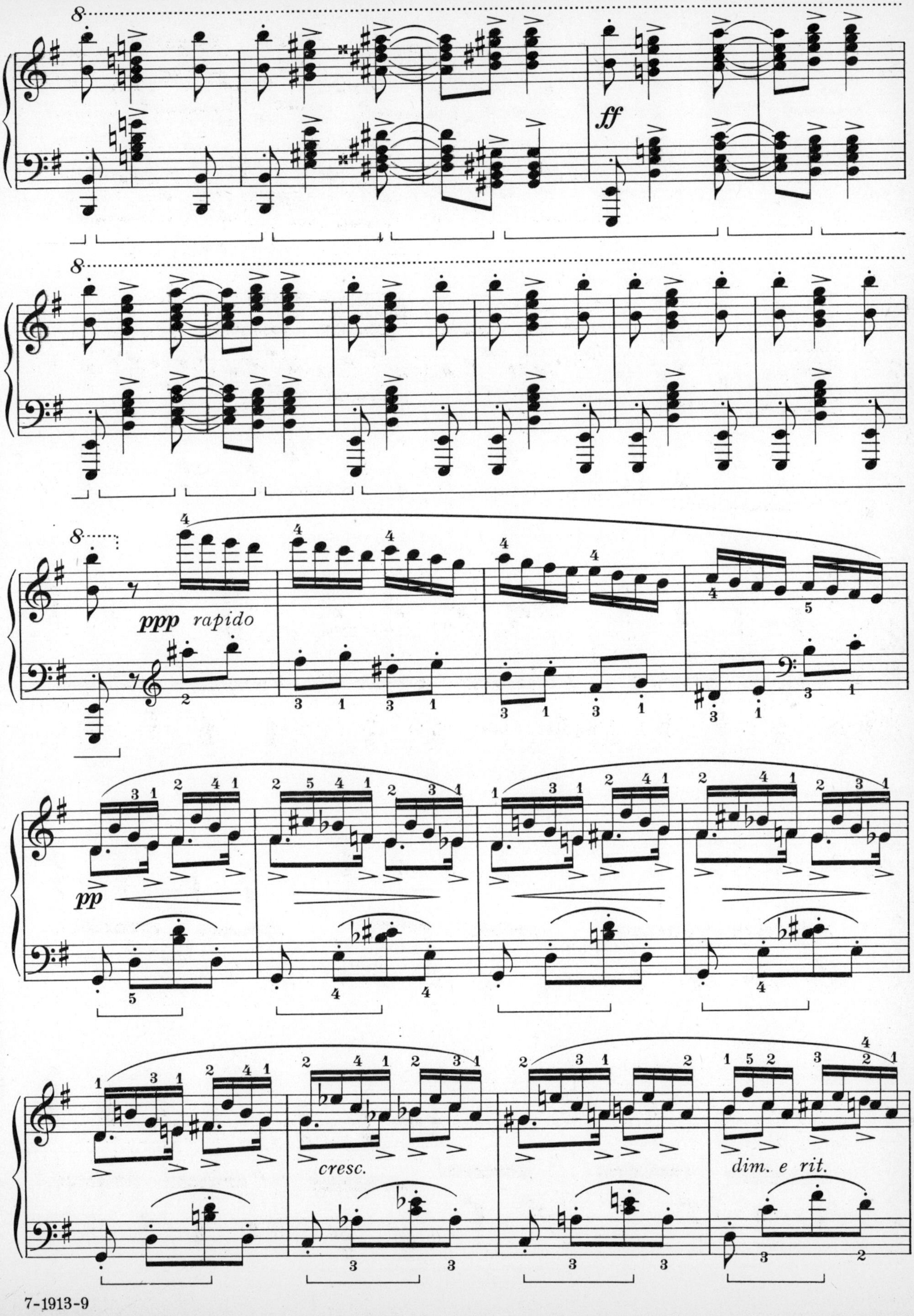

ff
ppp rapido
pp
cresc.
dim. e rit.

1660

1661

PRÉLUDE
C MAJOR

Edited by Charles Dennée

Fr. CHOPIN
Op. 28, No. 1

PRELUDE

Fr. CHOPIN
Op. 28, No 3

1664

PRELUDE

Fr. CHOPIN
Op 28, N°16

Presto con fuoco

1666

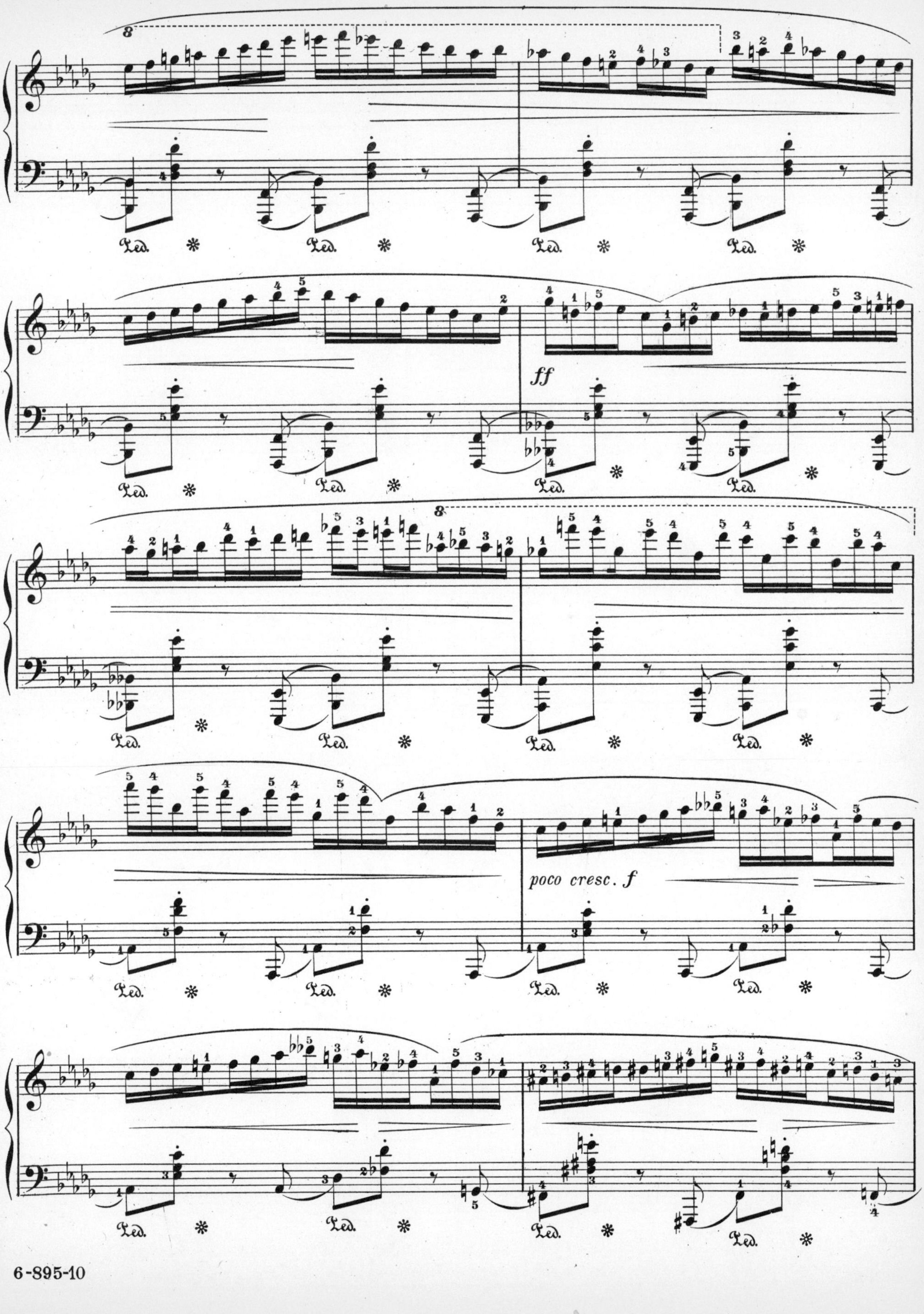
ff
poco cresc. f

1668

sempre più f

PRELUDE
B FLAT MAJOR

Fr. CHOPIN, Op. 28 No 21

1671

Six Poems after Heine

I
THE FISHER'S COTTAGE

Wir sassen am Fischerhause Und schauten nach der See; Die Abendnebel kamen Und stiegen in die Höh'.	We sat by the fisher's cottage, And looked at the stormy tide; The evening mist came rising, And floating far and wide.
Im Leuchtturm wurden die Lichter Allmählig angesteckt, Und in der weiten Ferne Ward noch ein Schiff entdeckt.	One by one in the light-house The lamps shone out on high; And far on the dim horizon A ship went sailing by.
Wir sprachen von fernen Küsten, Vom Süden und vom Nord; Und von den seltsamen Völkern Und seltsamen Sitten dort.	We spoke of storm and shipwreck,.. Of sailors, and how they live; Of journeys 'twixt sky and water, And the sorrows and joys they give.
Am Ganges duftet's und leuchtet's, Und Riesenbäume blüh'n, Und schöne, stille Menschen Vor Lotosblumen knieen.	Of perfumed lamps on the Ganges, Which are launched in the twilight hour; And the dark and silent Brahmins, Who worship the lotos flower.
Die Mädchen horchten ernsthaft, Und endlich sprach niemand mehr; Das Schiff war nicht mehr sichtbar, Es dunkelte gar zu sehr.	And the maidens earnestly listened, Till at last we spoke no more; The ship like a shadow had vanished, And darkness fell deep on the shore.

From the German of Heinrich Heine.
Translation by CHARLES G. LELAND.

EDWARD MacDOWELL
Op. 31, No. 1

1673

mf
ff
p subito poco a poco rall.
a tempo
dolce
8
8
p
rall.
pp
dolcigs.
slargando
ten.
ten.
molto rall.
m.s.

II
SCOTCH POEM

Fern an schottischer Felsenküste,
Wo das graue Schlösslein hinaus ragt
Über die brandende See,
Dort, am hochgewölbten Fenster,
Steht eine schöne, kranke Frau,
Zartdurchsichtig und marmorblass,
Und sie spielt die Harfe und singt,
Und der Wind durchwühlt ihre langen Locken
Und trägt ihr dunkles Lied
Über das weite, stürmende Meer.

Far away on the rock-coast of Scotland,
Where the old grey castle projecteth
Over the wild raging sea,
There at the lofty and arched window,
Standeth a woman beauteous, but ill,
Softly-transparent and marble pale;
And she's playing her harp and she's singing,
And the wind through her long locks forceth its way,
And beareth her gloomy song
Over the wide and tempest-tossed sea.

Translation from "Heine Complete"
by EDGAR ALFRED BOWRING, C.B.

EDWARD MacDOWELL
Op. 31, No. 2

Allegro tempestoso

due Ped.

sempre cresc.

ff

sempre cresc.
fff risoluto
pp subito
cresc.
ff brioso
marcatiss.
poco - a -
poco - - dim. - e - - rall.
molto rall. - -

Andante, a piacere
pp parlando, ma come da lontano
quasi arpa
pp
pp
molto rall.
perdendosi - - - -
Tempo I
ppp
f
sempre cresc.

ff
fff risoluto
brioso
marcatiss.
rall.
Andante
molto rall.
ppp
morendo

III
MY CHILD, WE ONCE WERE CHILDREN

Mein Kind, wir waren Kinder,
Zwei Kinder, klein und froh;
Wir krochen ins Hühnerhäuschen,
Versteckten uns unter das Stroh.

Des Nachbars alte Katze
Kam öfters zum Besuch;
Wir machten ihr Bücklinge und Knixe
Und Komplimente genug.

Vorbei sind die Kinderspiele,
Und alles rollt vorbei,-
Das Geld und die Welt und die Zeiten,
Und Glauben und Lieb' und Treu'.

My child, we once were children,
Two children little and gay;
We crawl'd inside the henhouse,
And hid in the straw in play.

The aged cat of our neighbor
Came oft to visit us there;
We made her our bows and our curtsies,
And plenty of compliments fair.

Those childish sports have vanish'd,
And all is fast rolling away;
The world and the times, and religion,
And gold, love and truth all decay.

Translation from "Heine Complete"
by EDGAR ALFRED BOWRING, C.B.

EDWARD MacDOWELL
Op. 31, No. 3

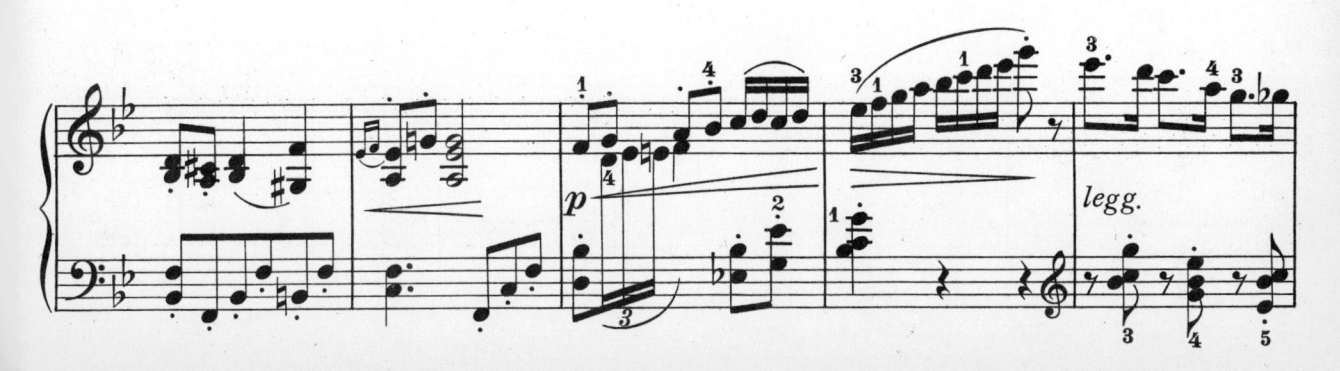

1680

1681

IV
IN THE POST-CHAISE

Wir fuhren allein im dunkeln
Postwagen die ganze Nacht;
Wir ruhten einander am Herzen,
Wir haben gescherzt und gelacht.

Doch als es morgens tagte,
Mein Kind, wie staunten wir!
Denn zwischen uns sass Amor,
Der blinde Passagier.

We travelled alone in the gloomy
Post-chaise the whole of the night;
Each lean'd on the other's bosom,
And jested with hearts so light.

When morning dawn'd upon us,
My child, how we did stare,
For the blind passenger,* "Amor",
Was sitting between us there!

Translation from "Heine Complete"
by EDGAR ALFRED BOWRING, C.B.

EDWARD MacDOWELL
Op. 31, No. 4

* A "blind passenger" in German means one who travels without paying his fare.

1683

ppp dolciss. ma sempre allegro

2 Ped.

ten.

ten.

pp

1684

1685

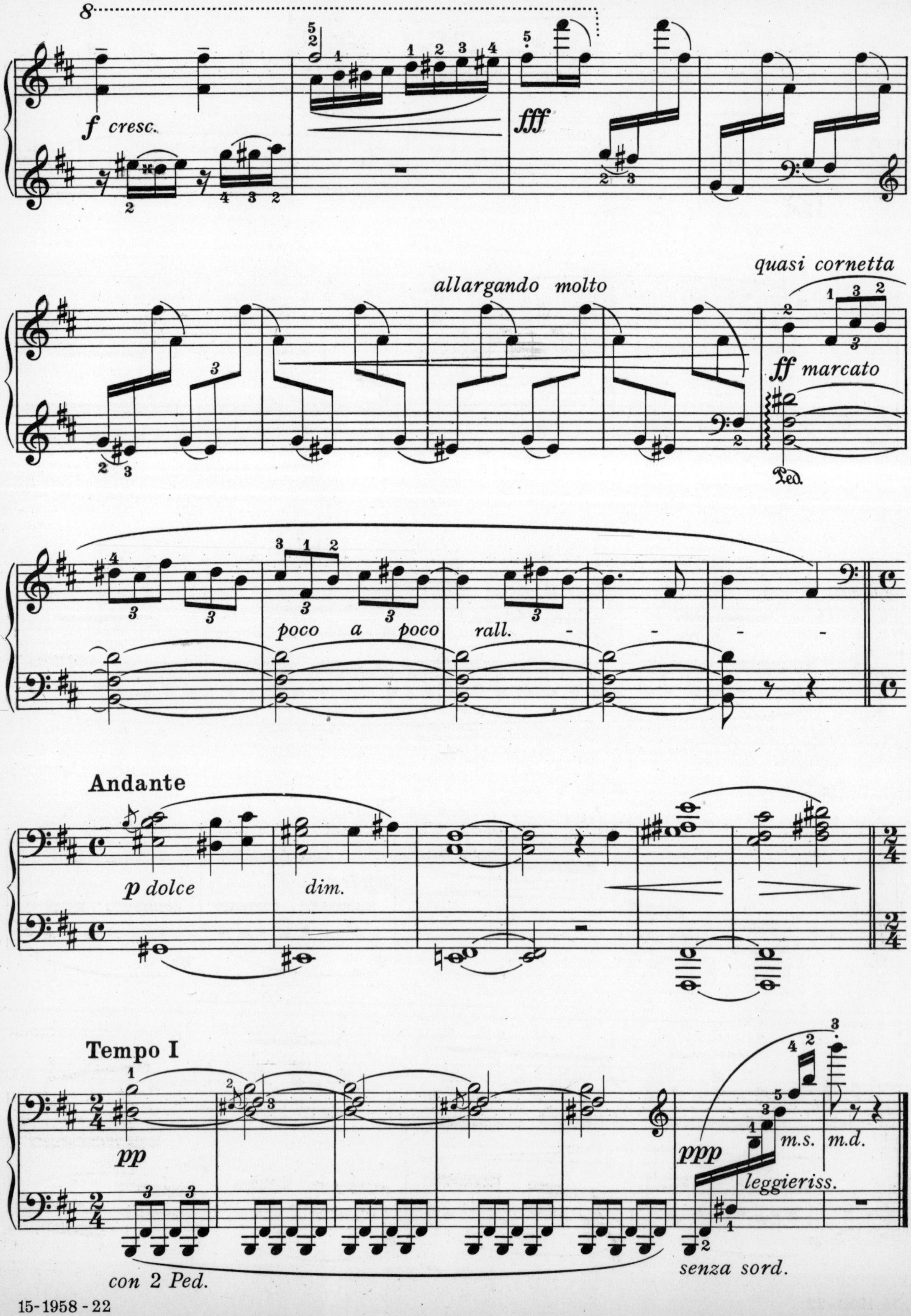
8
f cresc.
fff
allargando molto
quasi cornetta
ff marcato
Ped.
poco a poco rall.
Andante
p dolce
dim.
Tempo I
pp
ppp
m.s.
m.d.
leggieriss.
con 2 Ped.
senza sord.

V
THE SHEPHERD BOY

König ist der Hirtenknabe,
Grüner Hügel ist sein Thron;
Über seinem Haupt die Sonne
Ist die grosse, goldne Kron'.

Ihm zu Füssen liegen Schafe,
Weiche Schmeichler, rotbekreuzt;
Kavaliere sind die Kälber,
Und sie wandeln stelzgespreizt.

Hofschauspieler sind die Böcklein;
Und die Vögel und die Küh'
Mit den Flöten, mit den Glöcklein,
Sind die Kammermusici.

Schläfrig lallt der junge König;
„Das Regieren ist so schwer;
Ach, ich wollt', dass ich zu Hause
Schon bei meiner Kön'gin wär'!

„In den Armen meiner Kön'gin
Ruht mein Königshaupt so weich,
Und in ihren schönen Augen
Liegt mein unermesslich Reich!"

Shepherd-boy's a King,... on green hills
As a throne he sitteth down,
O'er his head the sun all radiant
Is his ever-golden crown.

At his feet the sheep are lying,
Gentle fawners, streak'd with red;
Calves as cavaliers attend him,
Proudly o'er the pastures spread.

Kids are all his court performers,
With the birds and cows as well,
And he has his chamber-music
To the sound of flute and bell.
. . . .
Sleepily the young King murmurs,
"'Tis a heavy task to reign;
Ah! right gladly would I find me
With my queen at home again!

"In my queen's arms soft and tender
Calmly rests my kingly head,
And my vast and boundless kingdom
In her dear eyes lies outspread."

Translation from "Heine Complete"
by EDGAR ALFRED BOWRING, C.B.

EDWARD MacDOWELL
Op. 31, No. 5

Allegretto placido

p dolce ma semplice

dolciss.
ten.
p
ten.
poco languido
dolentemente
poco rall.
pp dolciss.
cresc.
f
p

1689

VI
DEATH

Der Tod, das ist die kühle Nacht,
Das Leben ist der schwüle Tag,
Es dunkelt schon, mich schläfert,
Der Tag hat mich müd' gemacht.

Über mein Bett erhebt sich ein Baum,
Drin singt die junge Nachtigall;
Sie singt von lauter Liebe,
Ich hör' es sogar im Traum.

Death nothing is but cooling night,
And life is nought but sultry day;
Darkness draws nigh, I slumber,
Wearied by day's bright light.

Over my bed ariseth a tree,
There sings the youthful nightingale;
She sings of love exulting,
In dreams 'tis heard by me.

Translation from "Heine Complete"
by EDGAR ALFRED BOWRING, C.B.

EDWARD MacDOWELL
Op. 31, No. 6

1691

poco a poco rall.

pp

ppp   *rall.*

pp dolciss. mormorando

2 Ped. al Fine

1692

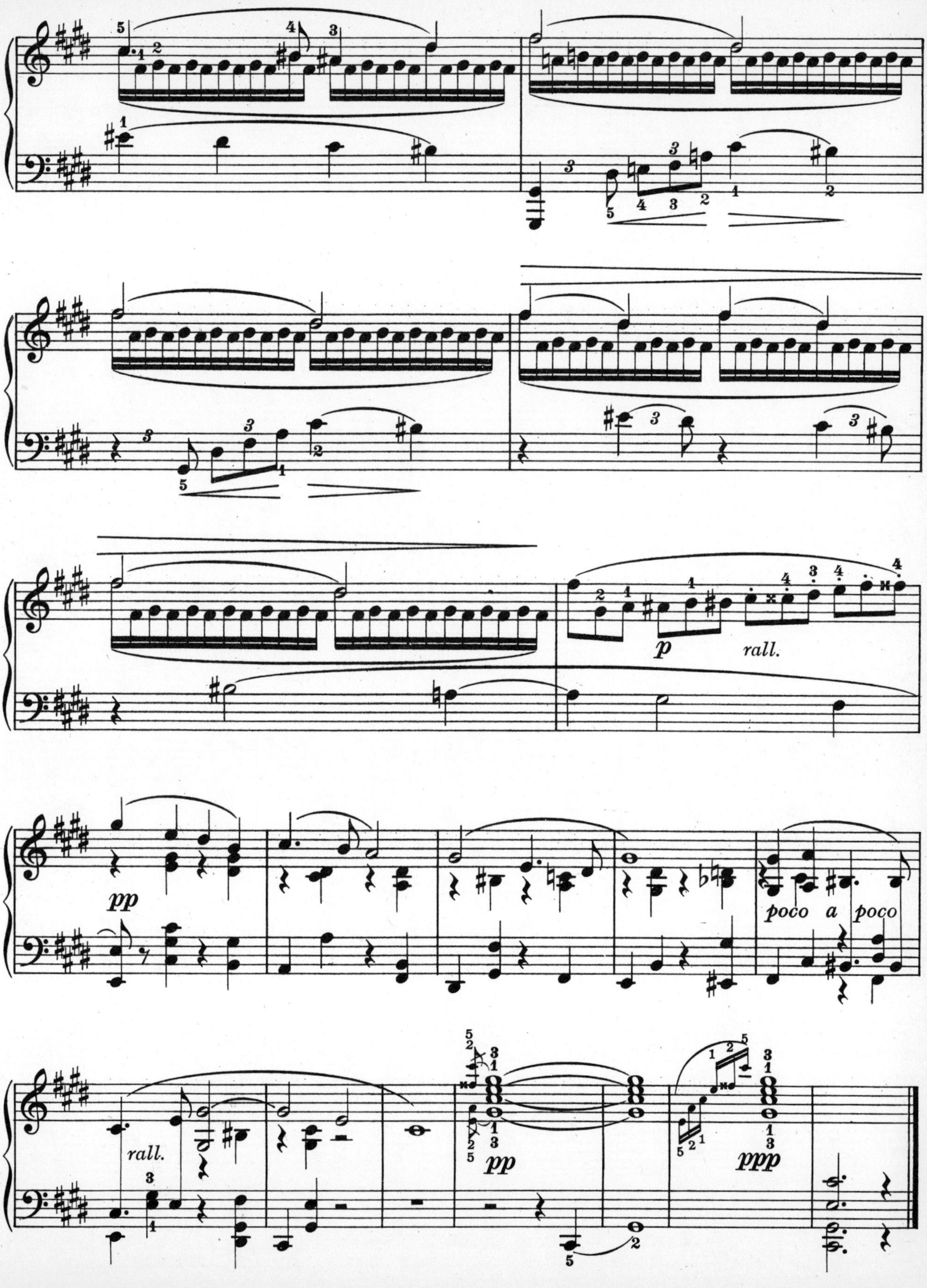
p
rall.
pp
poco a poco
rall.
pp
ppp

VALSE LENTE
(From "Coppélia")

Edited by
HENRY HOLDEN HUSS

LÉO DELIBES

1695

1696

1697

Più animato

INTERMEZZO
(From The Ballet "Naïla")

LEO DELIBES

1699

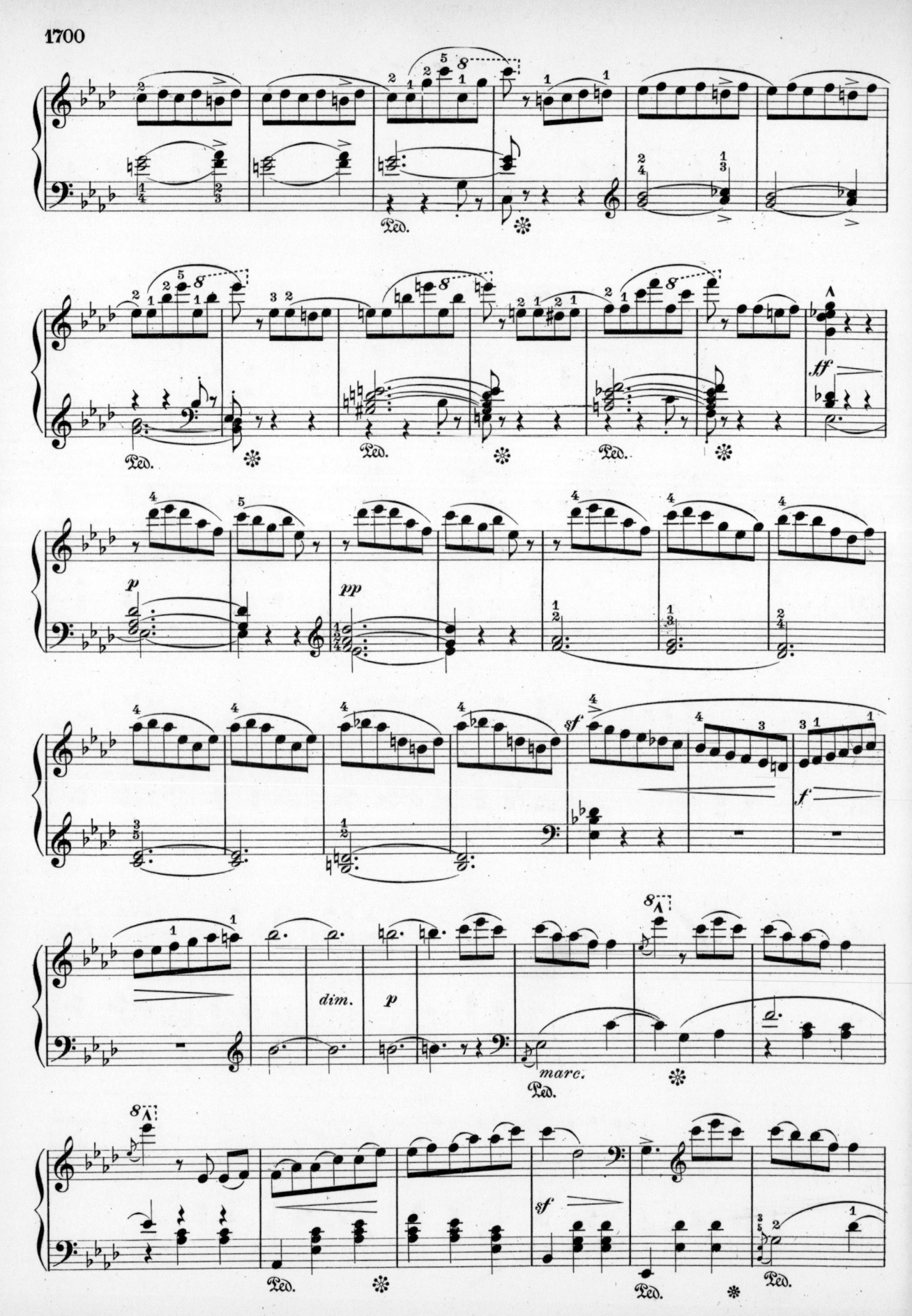
p
pp
ff
sf
f
dim.
marc.
Ped.

1701

1702

1703

1704

1705

IMPROMPTU
A-FLAT MAJOR

Edited by
Louis R. Dressler

HUGO REINHOLD
Op. 28, No 2

Con moto, moderato ma non troppo

1707

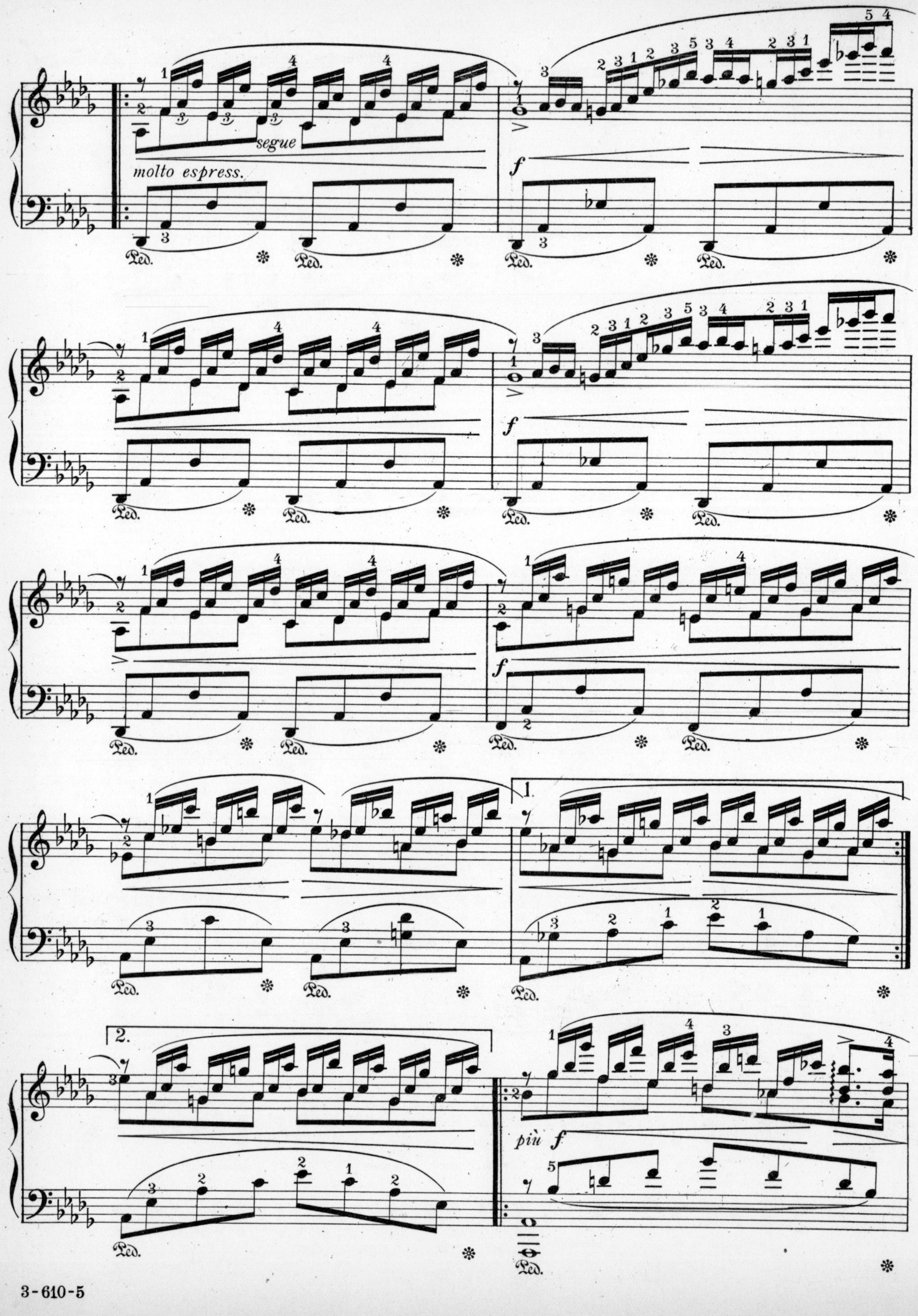
segue
molto espress.
f
Ped.
più f

1709

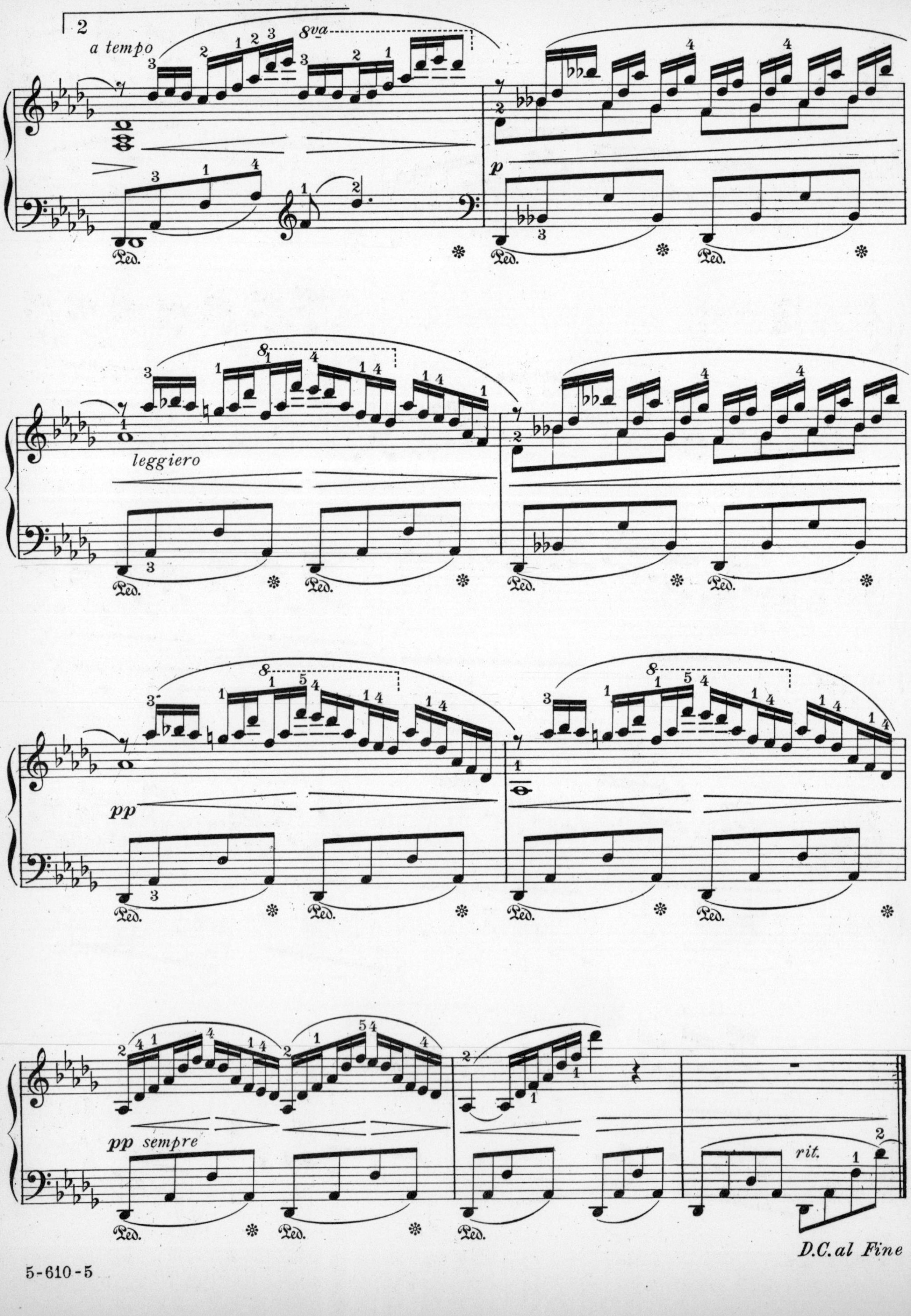
2
a tempo
8va
p
Ped.
leggiero
pp
pp sempre
rit.
D.C. al Fine

FUGUE IN E MINOR

From the CENTURY LIBRARY of MUSIC
Edited by Ignace J. Paderewski

HANDEL

Allegro

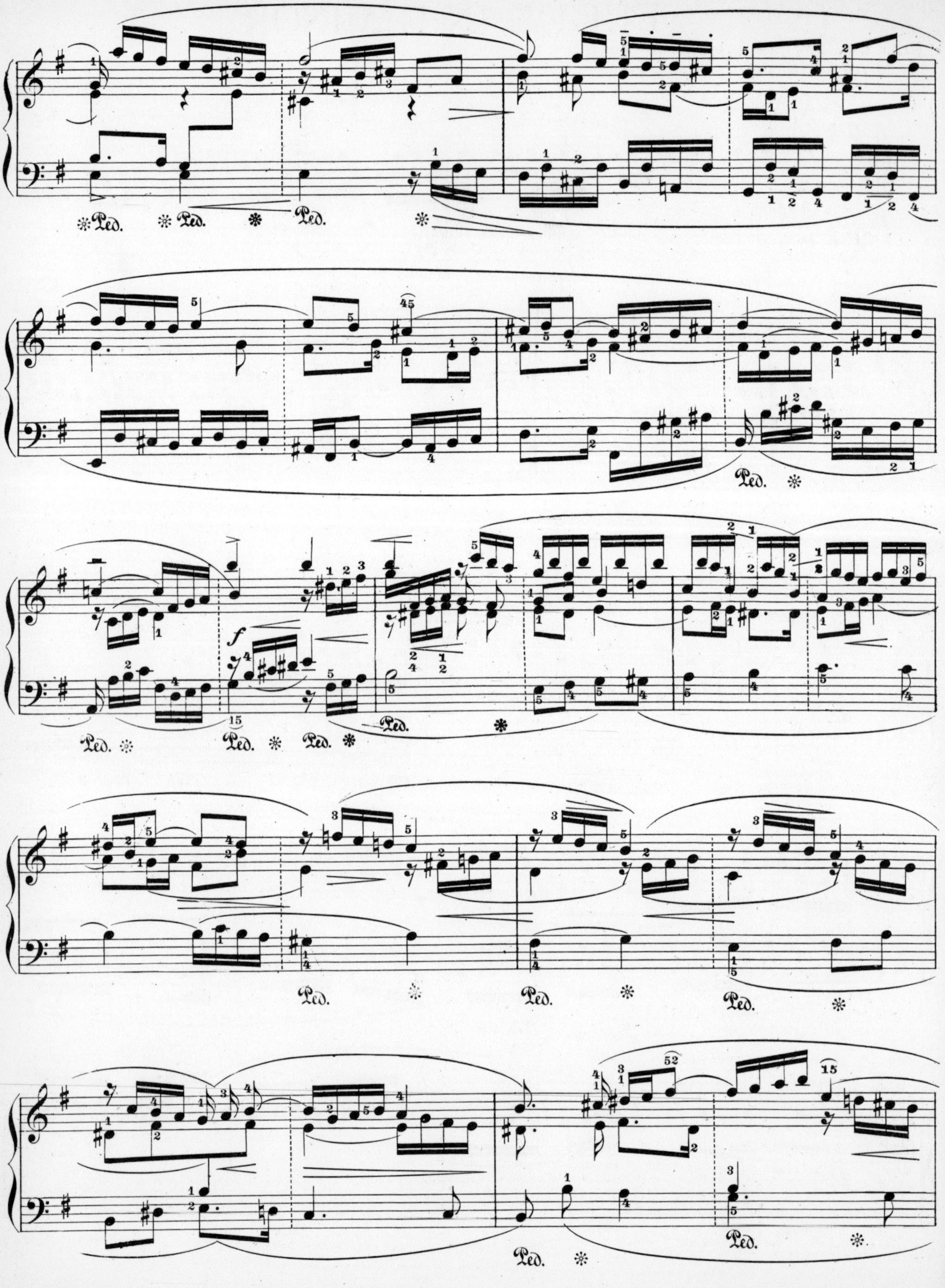
Ped.
Ped.
Ped.
Ped.
f
Ped.
Ped.
Ped.
Ped.
Ped.
Ped.
Ped.
Ped.
Ped.

1713

Ossia

1715

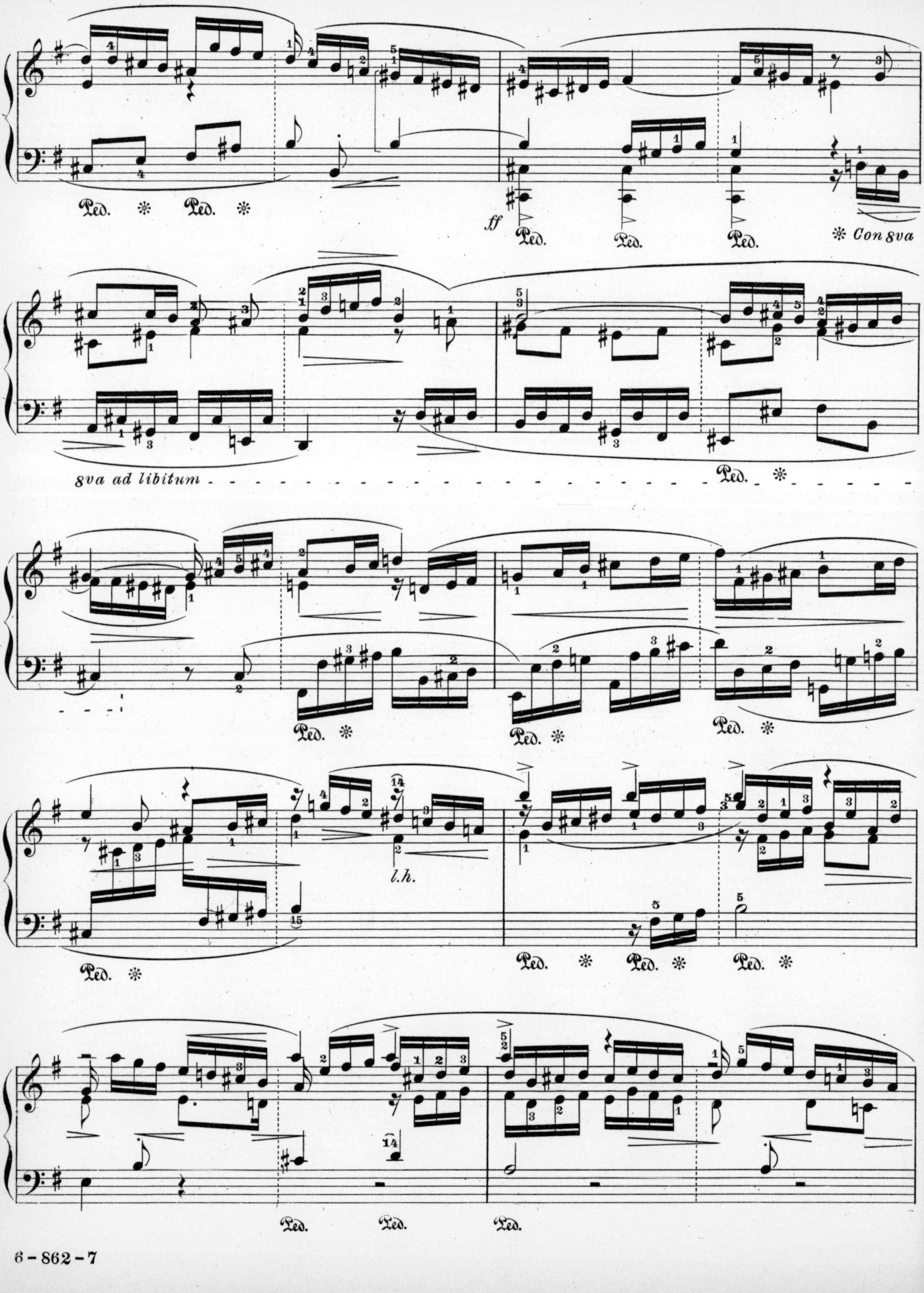
Ped.
ff
Con 8va
8va ad libitum
l.h.

1717

ITALIAN CONCERTO

Edited by
Mortimer Wilson

J. S. BACH

Allegro animato

1719

1720

1721

ten.
sempre piano
legato
espress.
132
f
p
cresc.
f cresc.
p
f
poco cresc.
dim.
p
cresc.
f calando

1723

cresc.
poco rit.
ff a tempo
sfz
ff
f
sempre f
marcato e sempre cresc.
con 8va ad lib.
non legato
più f
poco allargando
ff

Andante
p
Ped.
mf espressivo e cantabile
simile
p
cresc.
f
dim.
p

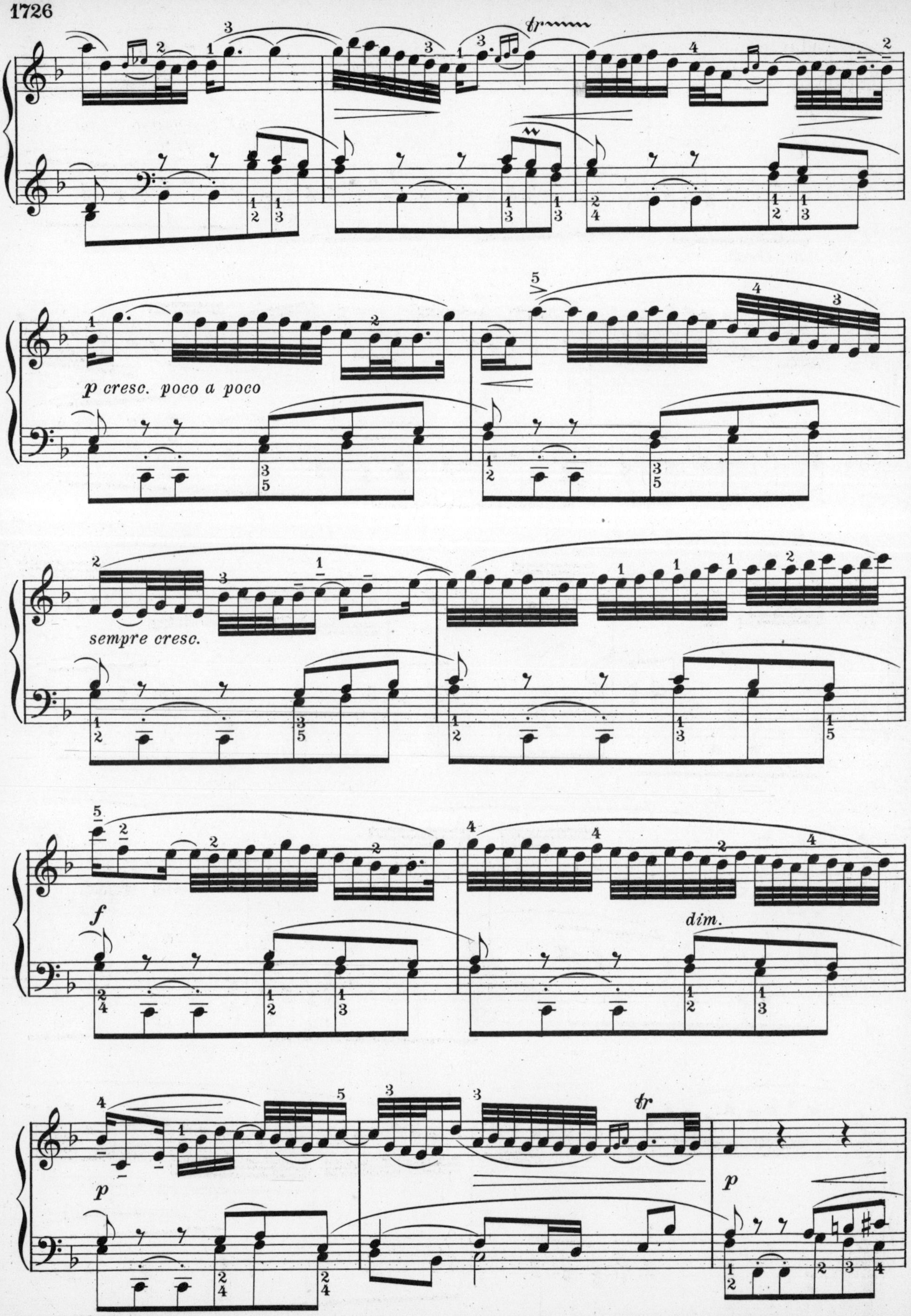
tr
p cresc. poco a poco
sempre cresc.
f
dim.
p
tr
p

1727

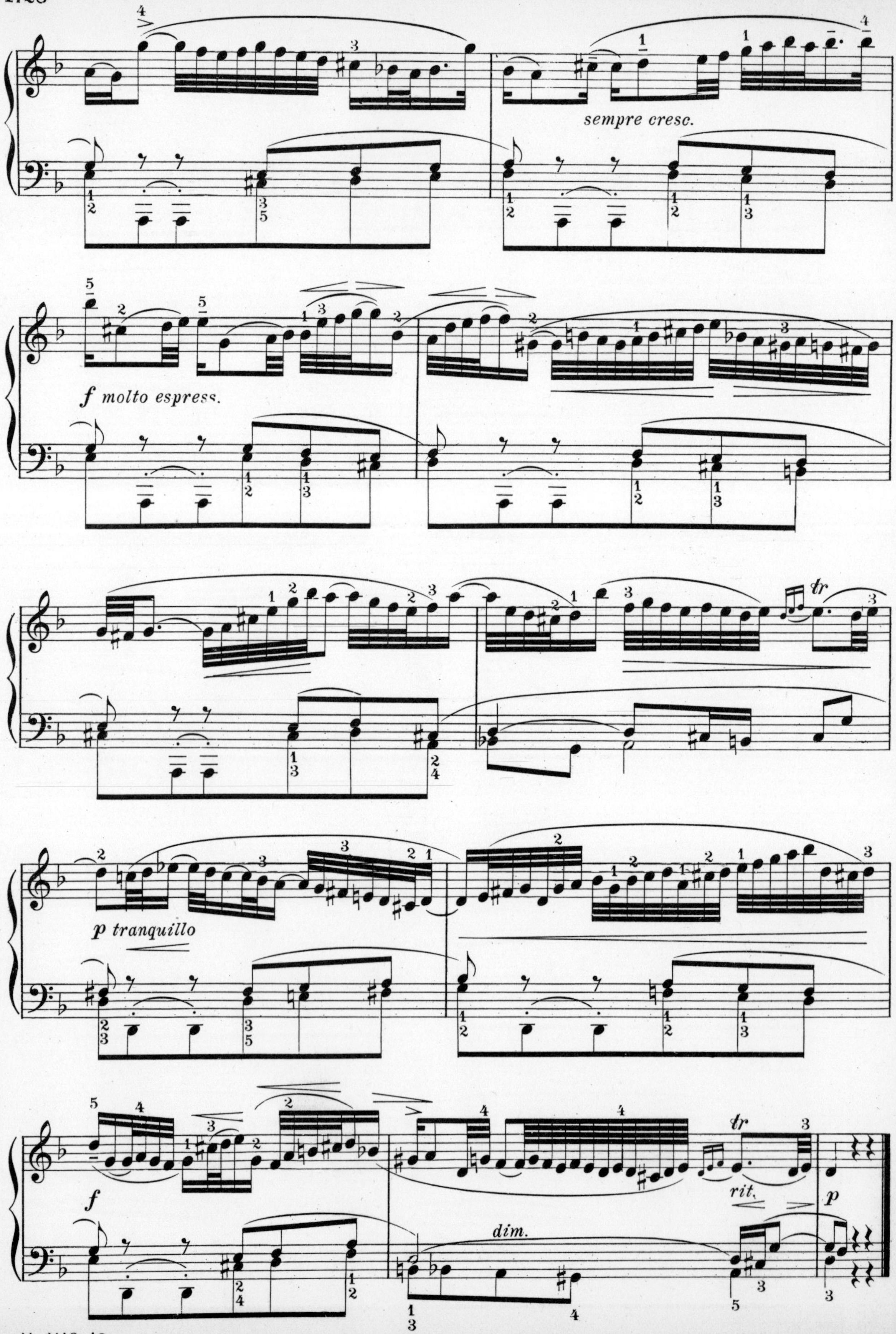
sempre cresc.
f molto espress.
tr
p tranquillo
f
dim.
tr
rit.
p

Presto giocoso

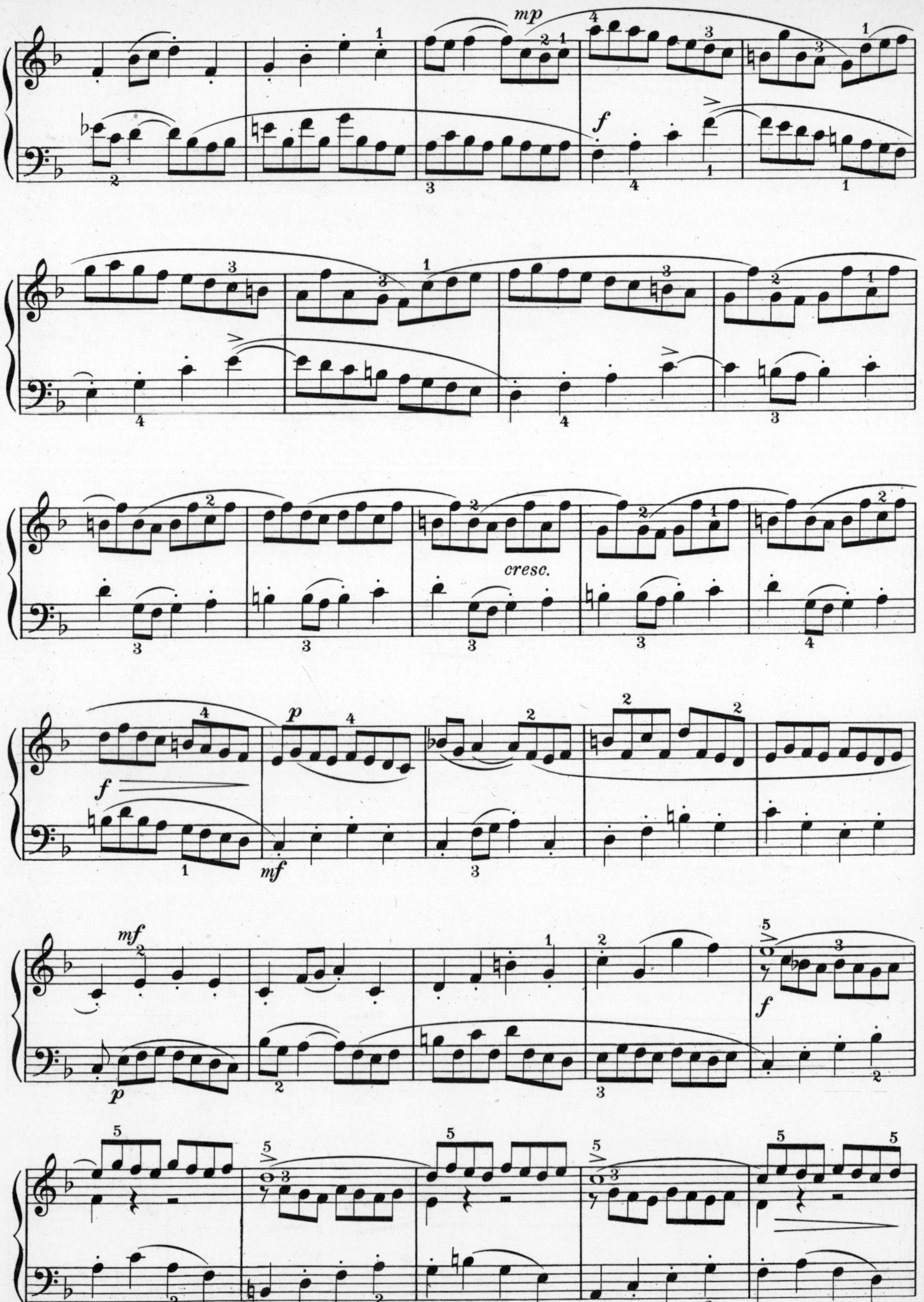
mp
f
cresc.
f
p
mf
mf
p
f

1731

1732

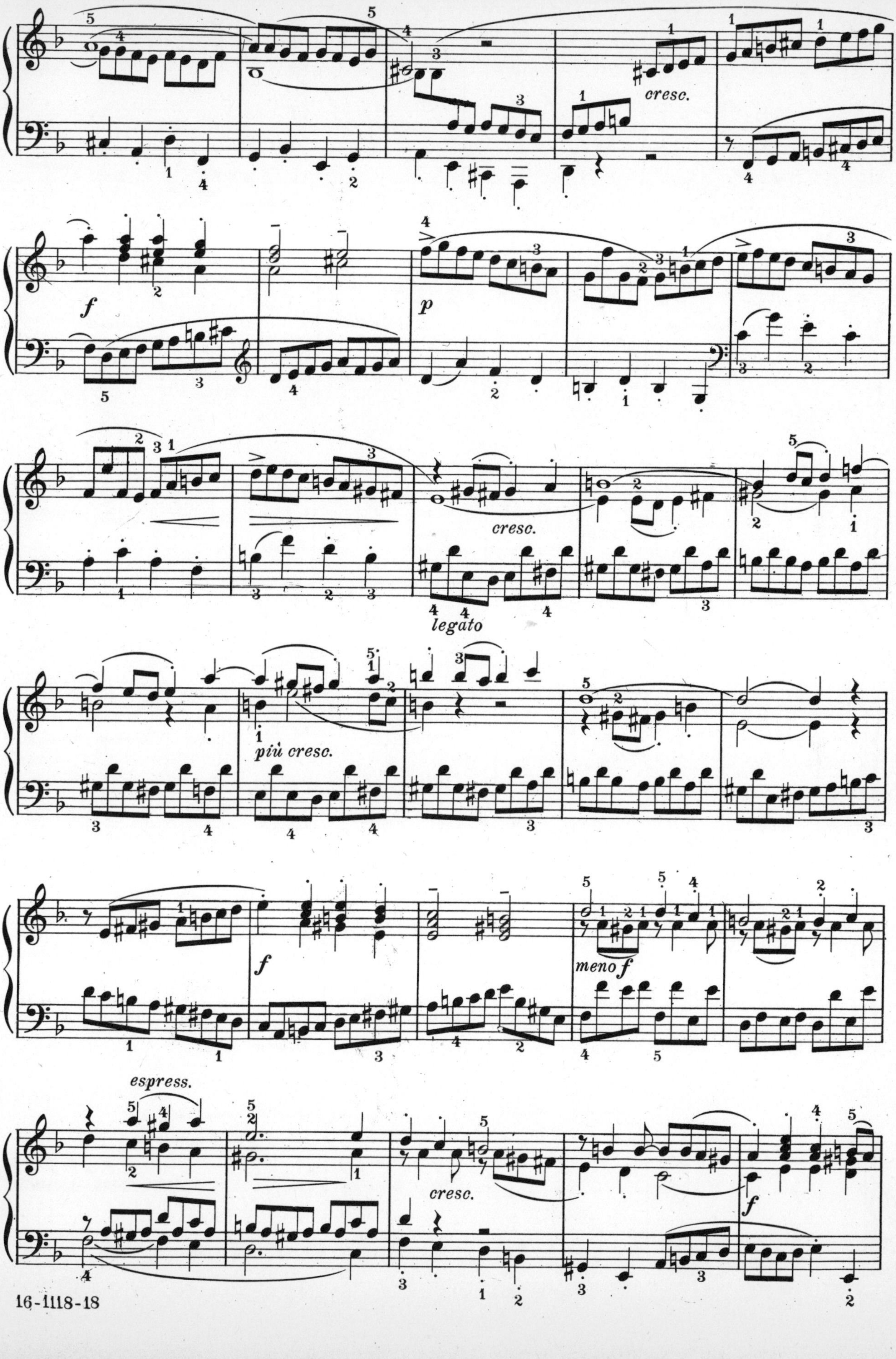
cresc.
f
p
cresc.
legato
più cresc.
f
meno f
espress.
cresc.
f

1734

1735

AUTOMNE
ETUDE DE CONCERT

Edited by
Nicholas de Vore

CÉCILE CHAMINADE,
Op. 35, No 2

Lento (♪ = 112)

Agitato

molto string.

1737

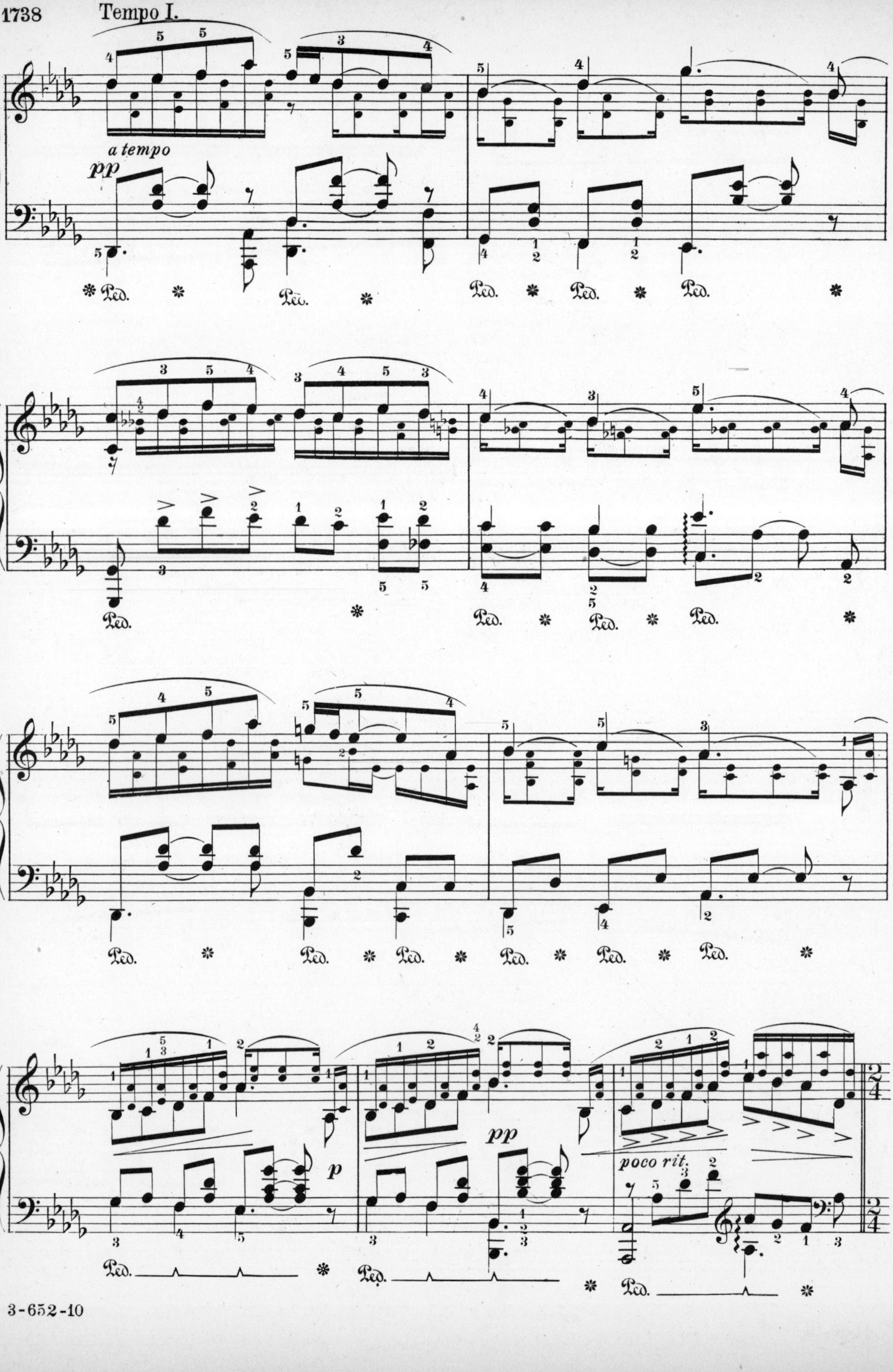
Tempo I.
a tempo
pp
Ped.
p
pp
poco rit.

1739

1740 Poco più largo, appassionato

1741

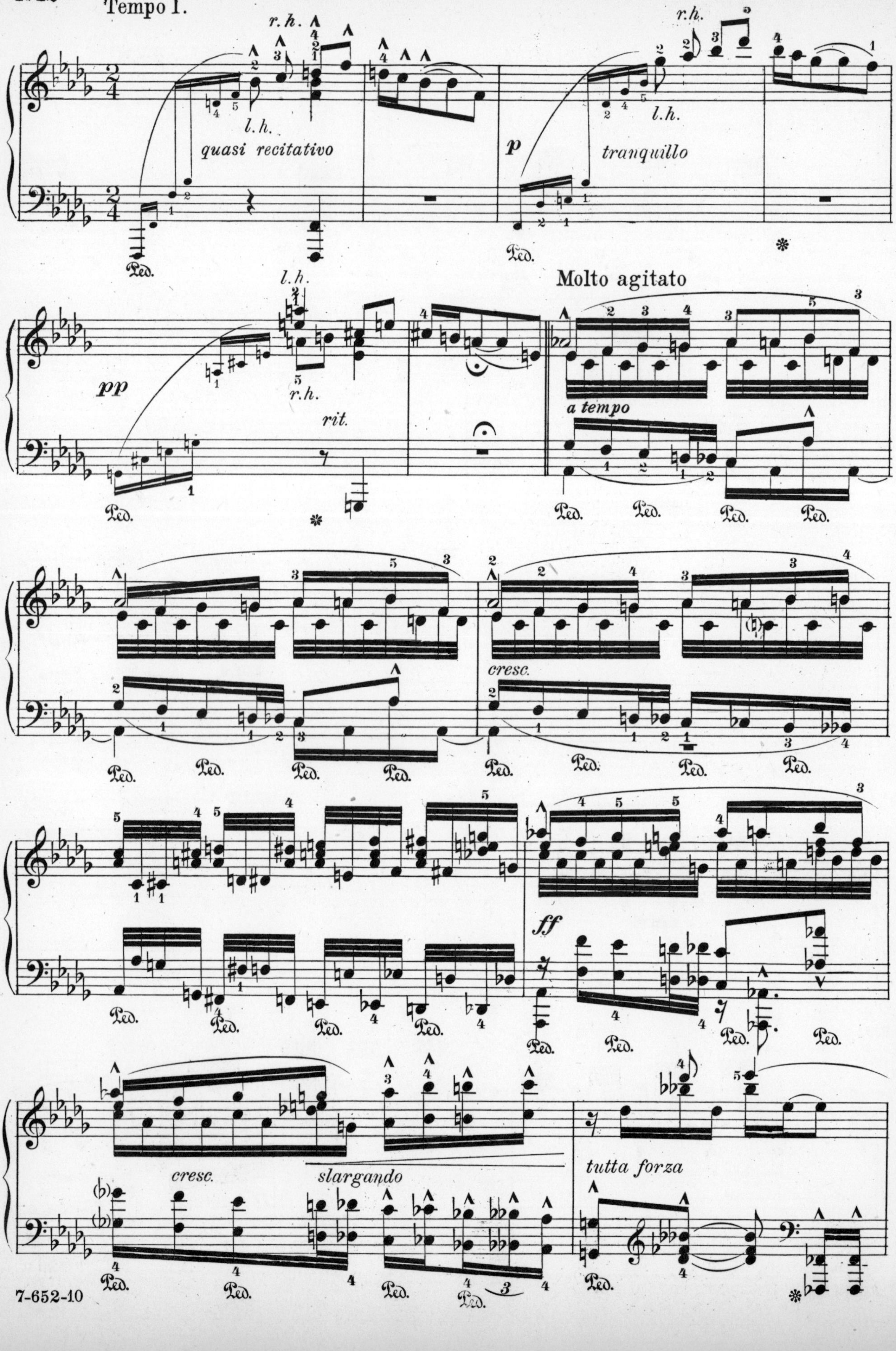
Tempo I.
r.h.
l.h.
quasi recitativo
p
tranquillo
Ped.
pp
rit.
Molto agitato
a tempo
cresc.
ff
slargando
tutta forza

1743

Agitato.

1745

VALSE
A-FLAT MAJOR

Edited by
Bern. Boekelman

CHOPIN
Op. 42

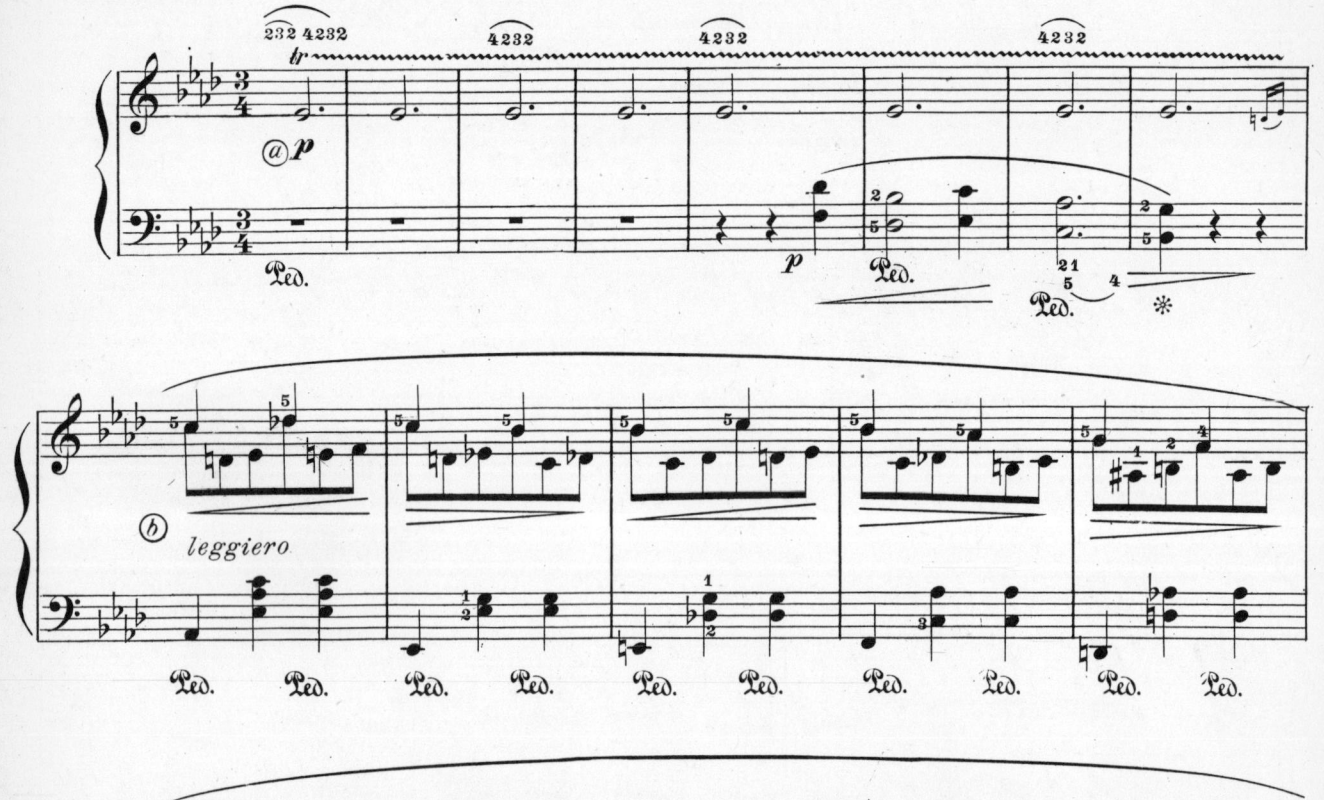

ⓐ — Chopin could not have intended a monotonous droning effect in this introduction. With respect to its execution, the quickness of the trill and its shading by crescendo and diminuendo is left to the taste of the player. The notes may be divided thus:

ⓑ — The melody of the principal theme is to be played with a *cantabile tenuto tone*, sung as it were in a clear voice; the accompaniment-figure is to be played *leggiero*. After playing a melody-tone, the requisite relaxation of the muscles of the hand and arm should be carefully observed. The rhythm of the left hand part must be very even, in order that the essential waltz movement (3/4 time) may be constantly kept in view, in spite of the feeling of 2/4 time in the right hand part.

ⓒ — In practising short trills like this, players, when the fingers do not answer promptly, often make the mistake of studying the trill by itself without connecting it with the passage following, something even more important. The trill must be executed crisply and sharply.

1748

(d) —This characteristic figure which, so to speak, haunts the whole piece like a beautiful apparition and constantly recurs as a surprise, will produce a charming effect, when executed according to the intention of the composer (indicated by *leggiero*) with a velvety touch and pianissimo throughout. Play the accompaniment in exact rhythm, and let the melody tones in the bass at ✲ (indicated by the tones marked thus >) be well pronounced.

(e) —The accompanying tones for the right hand are to be touched lightly.

The sharp contrasts in this part of the piece recurring in groups of two measures require a contrast in their execution. We venture to suggest, by the dynamic indications, *risoluto* (resolutely), *giocoso* (playfully), *energico* (energetically), and (*passionata*), a possible interpretation.

ⓖ —In this measure the upper tones of the accompaniment **are correctly** given as E♭, instead of F, as often erroneously printed. It is probable that a *tie* connecting G with the same tone in the next measure has been omitted by mistake. The melody should have a plaintive character, with an increase of passion, when later a second voice is added,—which latter should sing no less than the upper voice.

1751

(h) —It is not advisable here to diminish the tone quality, as otherwise the following three measures (the melody is somewhat altered rhythmically) would lose their peculiar character.

1753

ⓘ —The organpoint E♭ may be played so as to produce a droning effect, increasing to the climax of the passage-work indicated by a ✸ when the fundamental tone A♭ becomes the persistent sound.

(k) —We have modernized the closing figure by giving it in "blind" Octaves. The original stands thus:

INVITATION TO THE DANCE
AUFFORDERUNG ZUM TANZ
(Rondeau Brillant)

Concert Arrangement by Franz Liszt

CARL M. von WEBER, Op. 65.

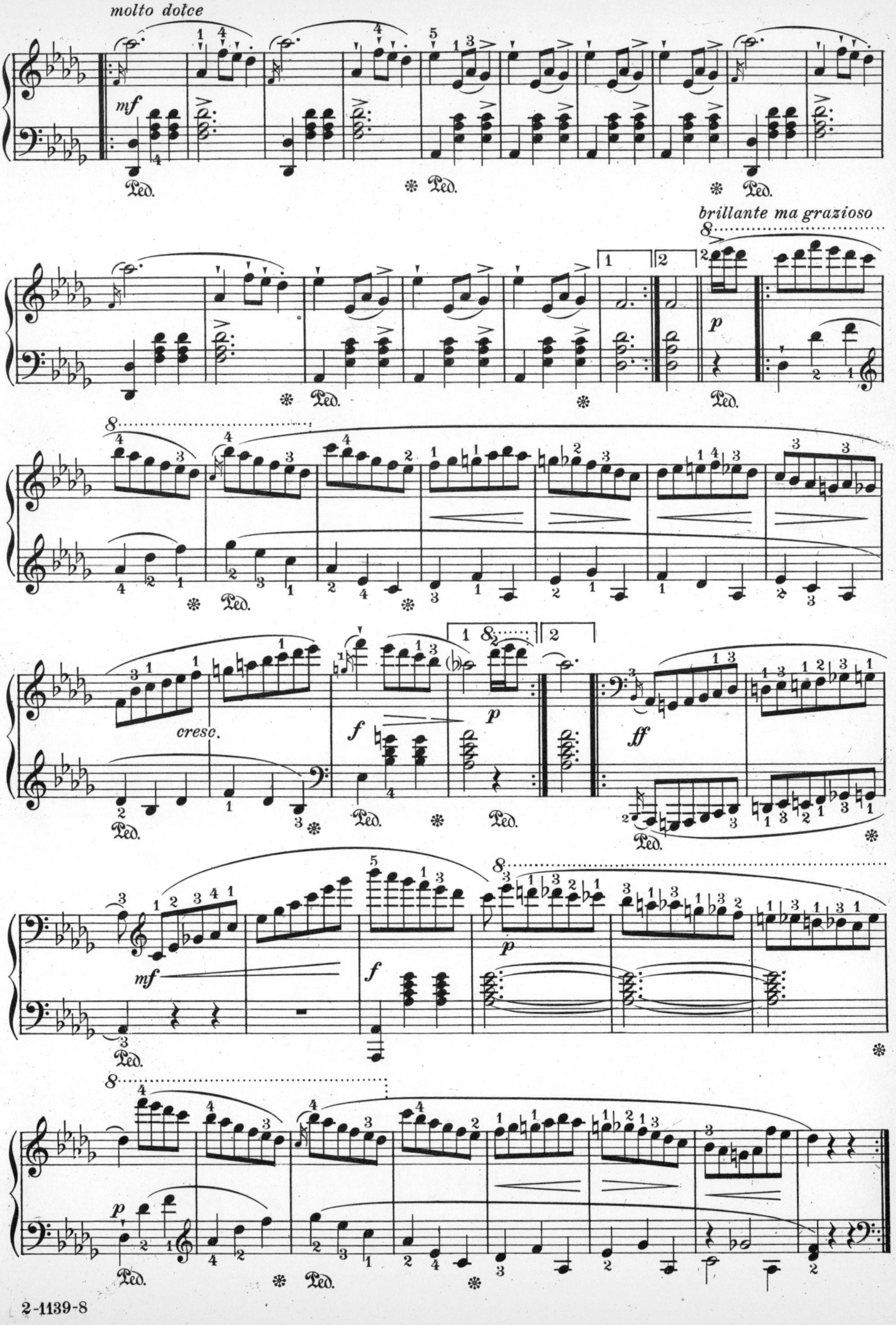
molto dolce
mf
Ped.
brillante ma grazioso
p
cresc.
f
ff
mf

1758

1759

1760

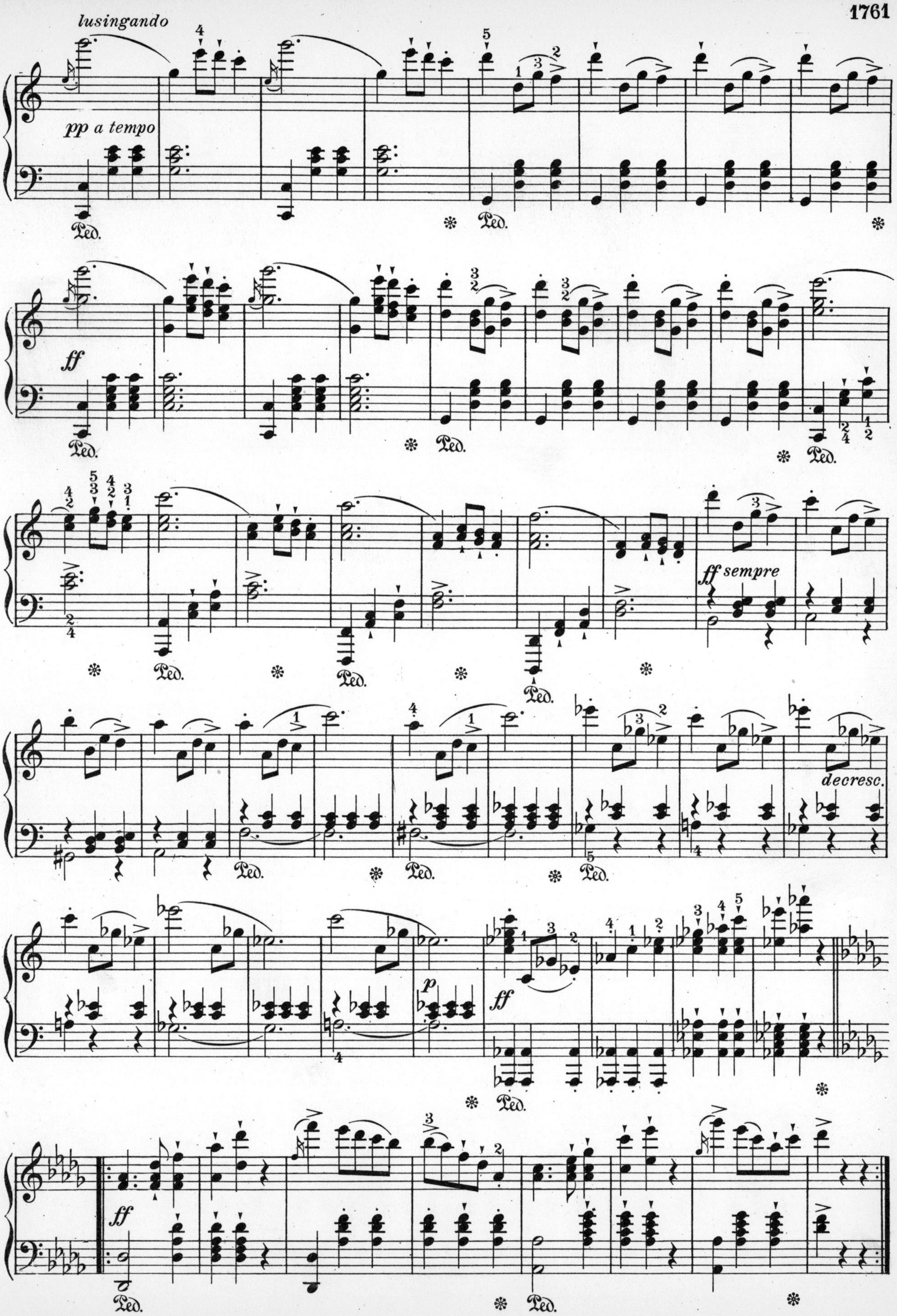
lusingando
pp a tempo
Ped.
ff
ff sempre
decresc.
p

1762

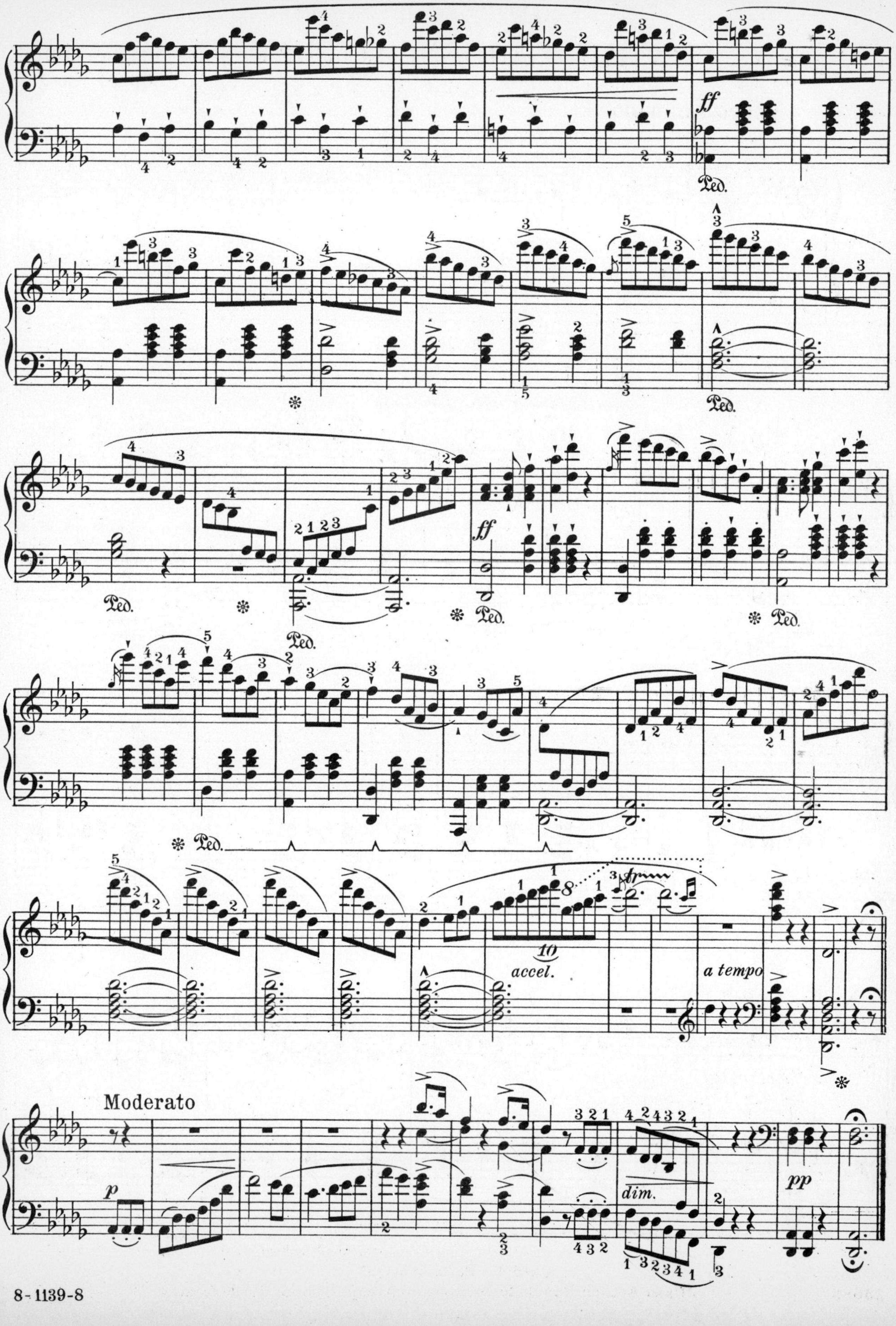
ff
Ped.
accel.
a tempo
Moderato
p
dim.
pp

IN THE GARDEN, AT PLAY

H. VILLA-LOBOS
Op. 97, n. 3

Pouco Animado

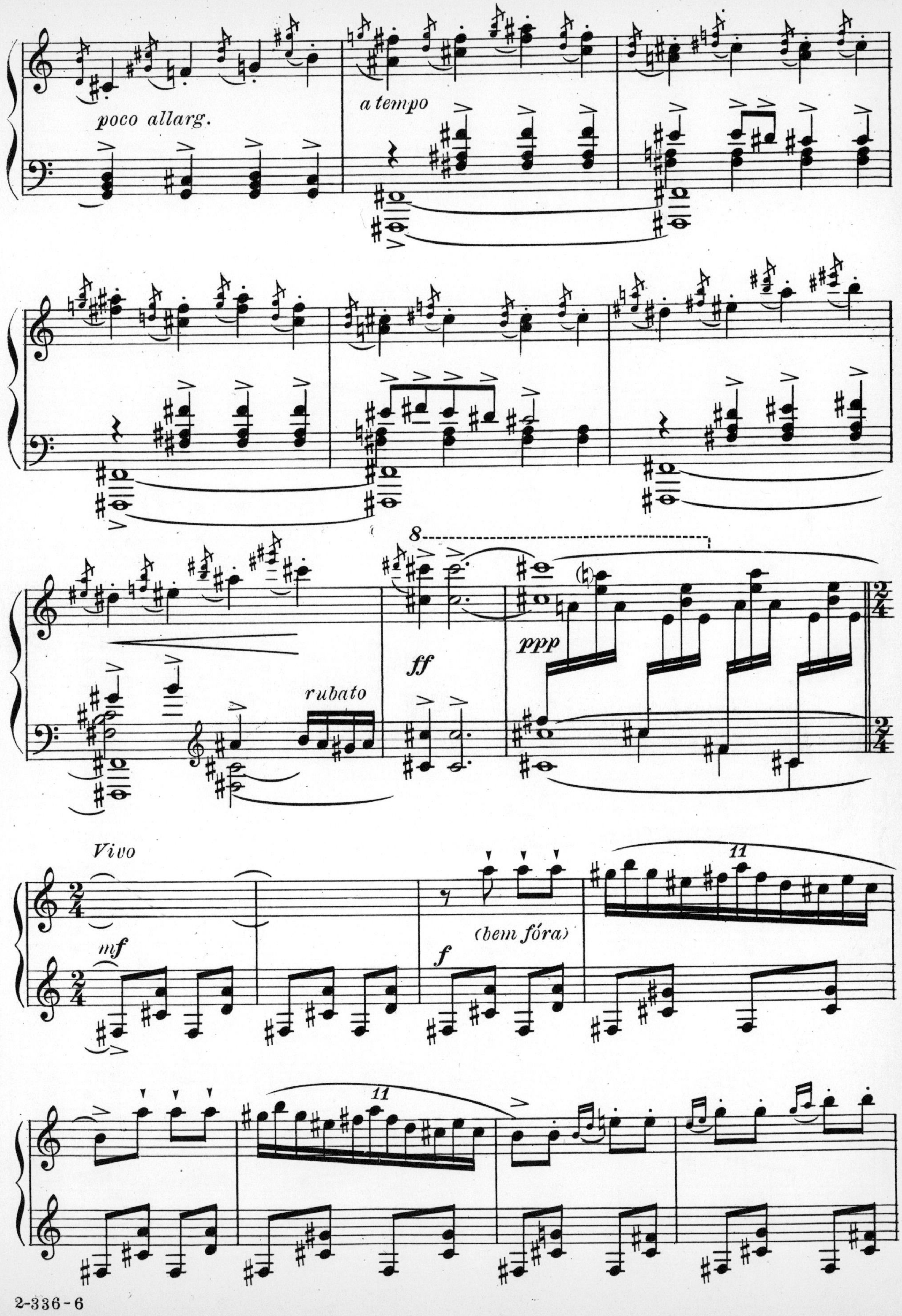
poco allarg.
a tempo
rubato
8
ff
ppp
Vivo
mf
f
(bem fóra)
11
11

(o baixo sempre bem marcado)

1767

cresc.
rall.
poco
Tempo I?
ff (um pouco grandeoso)
cresc.
rall.
fff a tempo
rall.
Tempo I?
sffz
sffz

1769

PRELUDE
G Minor

SERGEI RACHMANINOFF
Op. 23, No. 5

Alla marcia (♩= 92-108)

1771

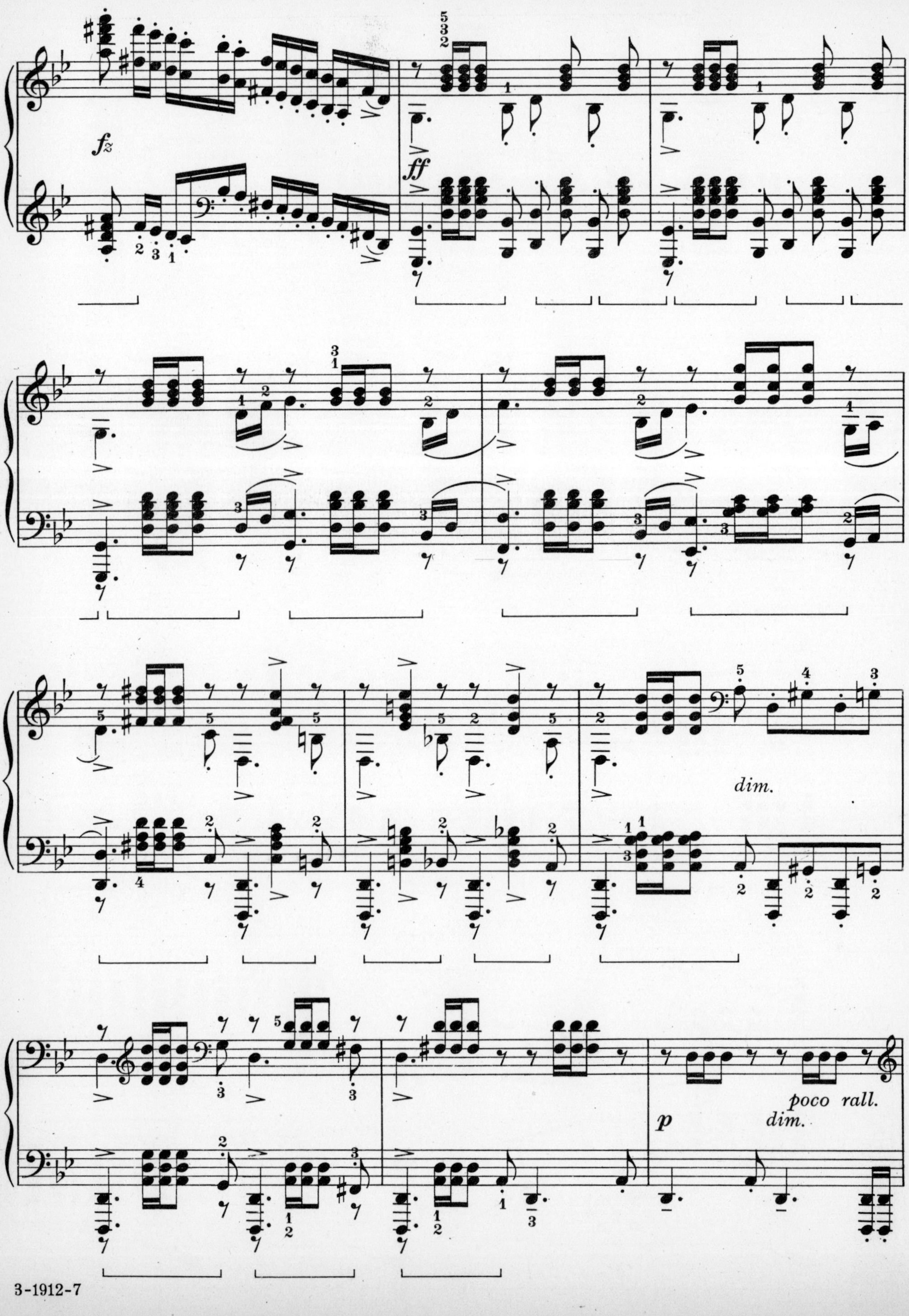
fz
ff
dim.
poco rall.
p
dim.

Un poco meno mosso ♩=72-78

poco a poco accelerando e cresc. al Tempo I

Tempo I

1776

SONATA
C MINOR
"Pathetique"

Edited by Charles Dennée

Grave (♩= 69)

L. van BEETHOVEN
Op. 13

(attacca subito l'Allegro).

Allegro molto, e con brio (𝅗𝅥 = 138)

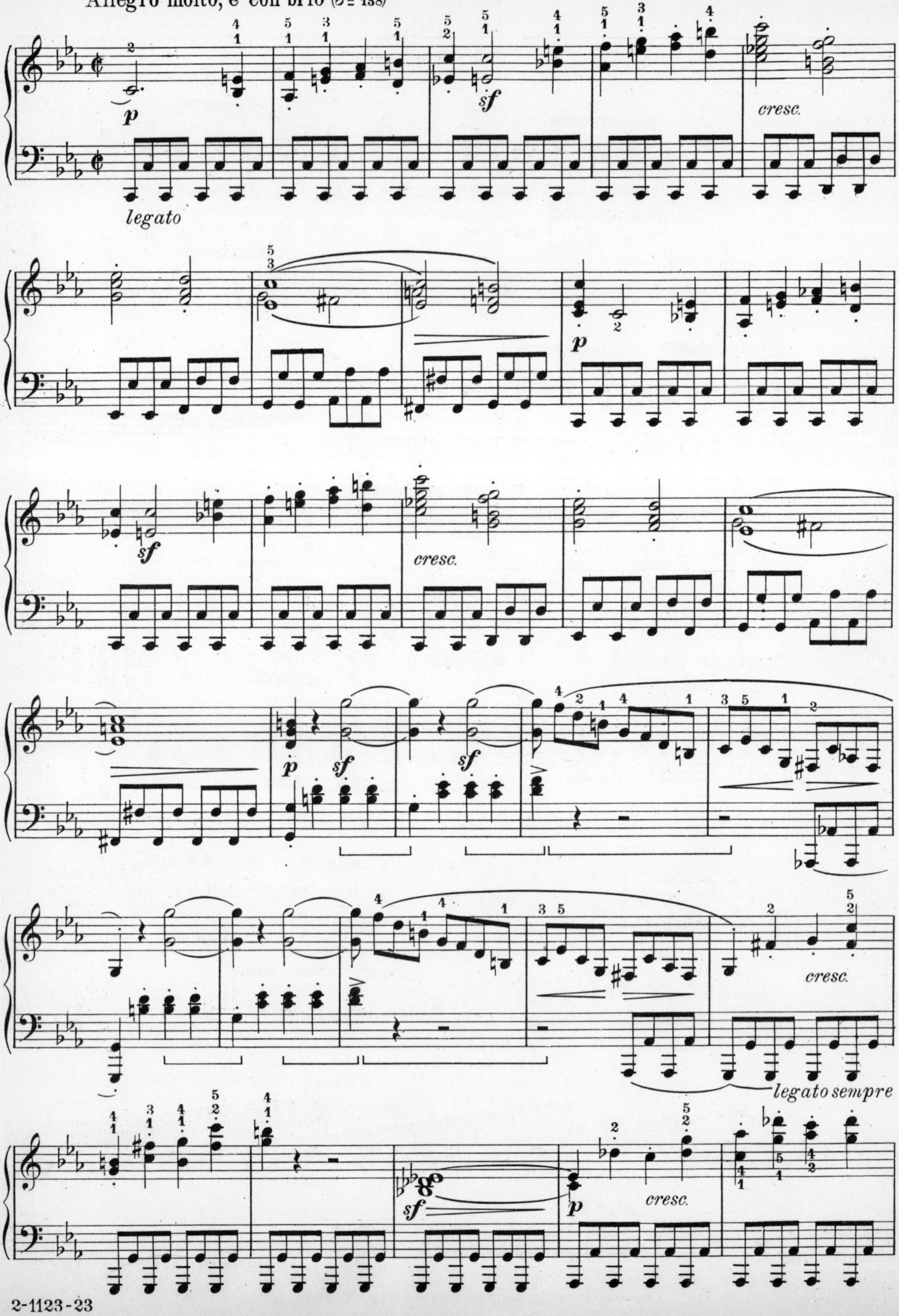

1779

1780

1781

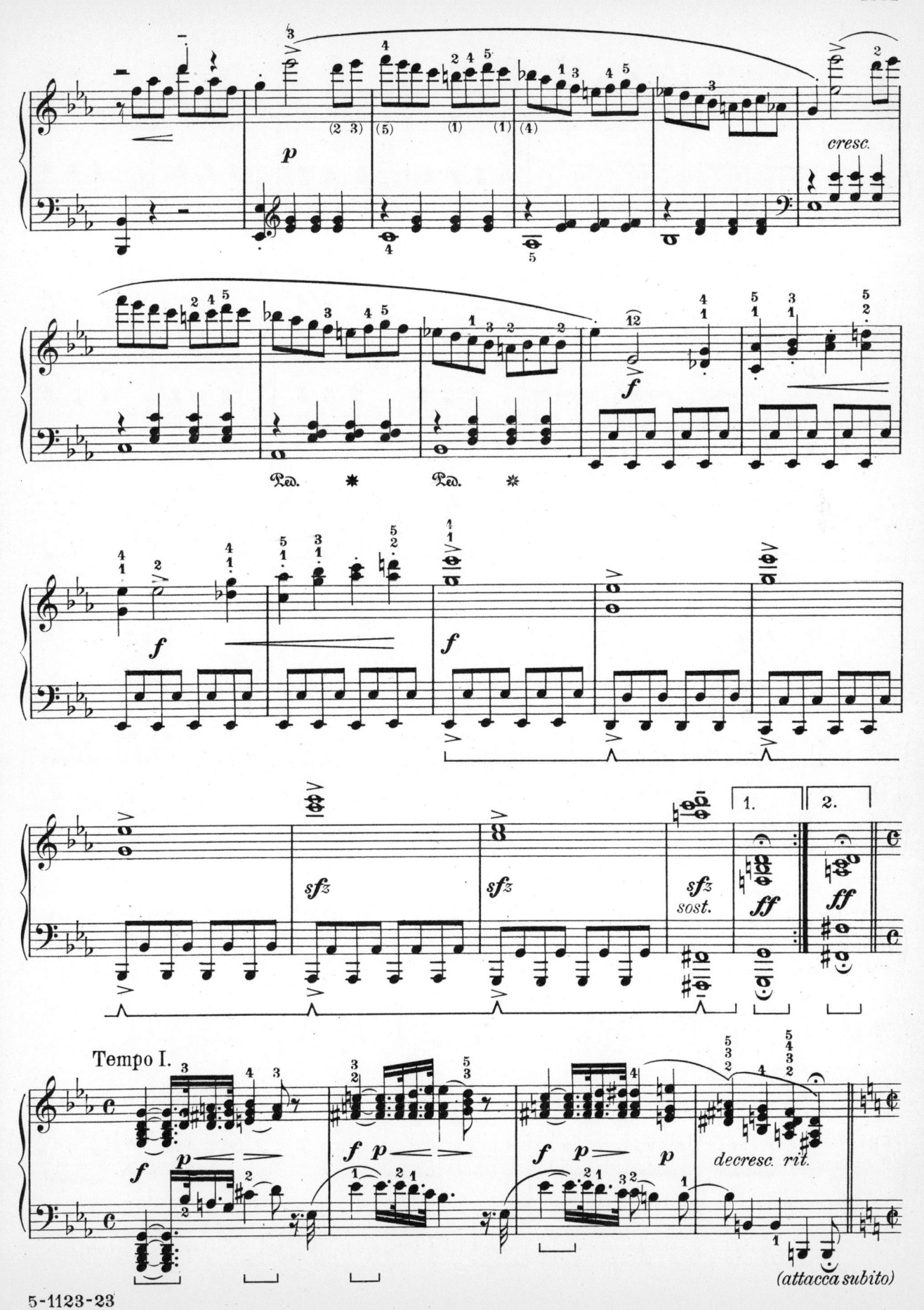

Allegro molto, e con brio

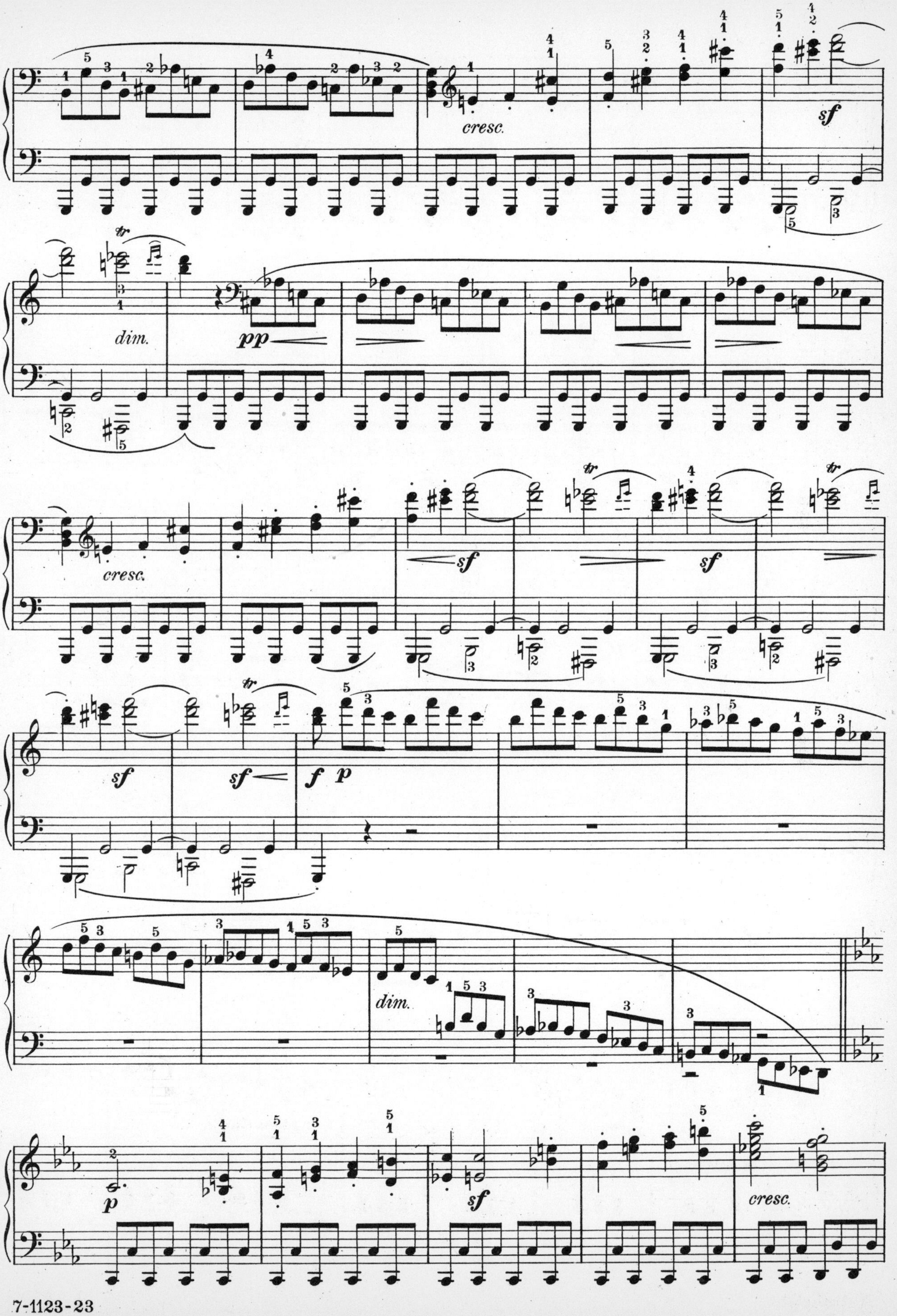
cresc.
sf
dim.
tr
pp
cresc.
sf
tr
sf
tr
sf
sf
tr
f
p
dim.
p
sf
cresc.

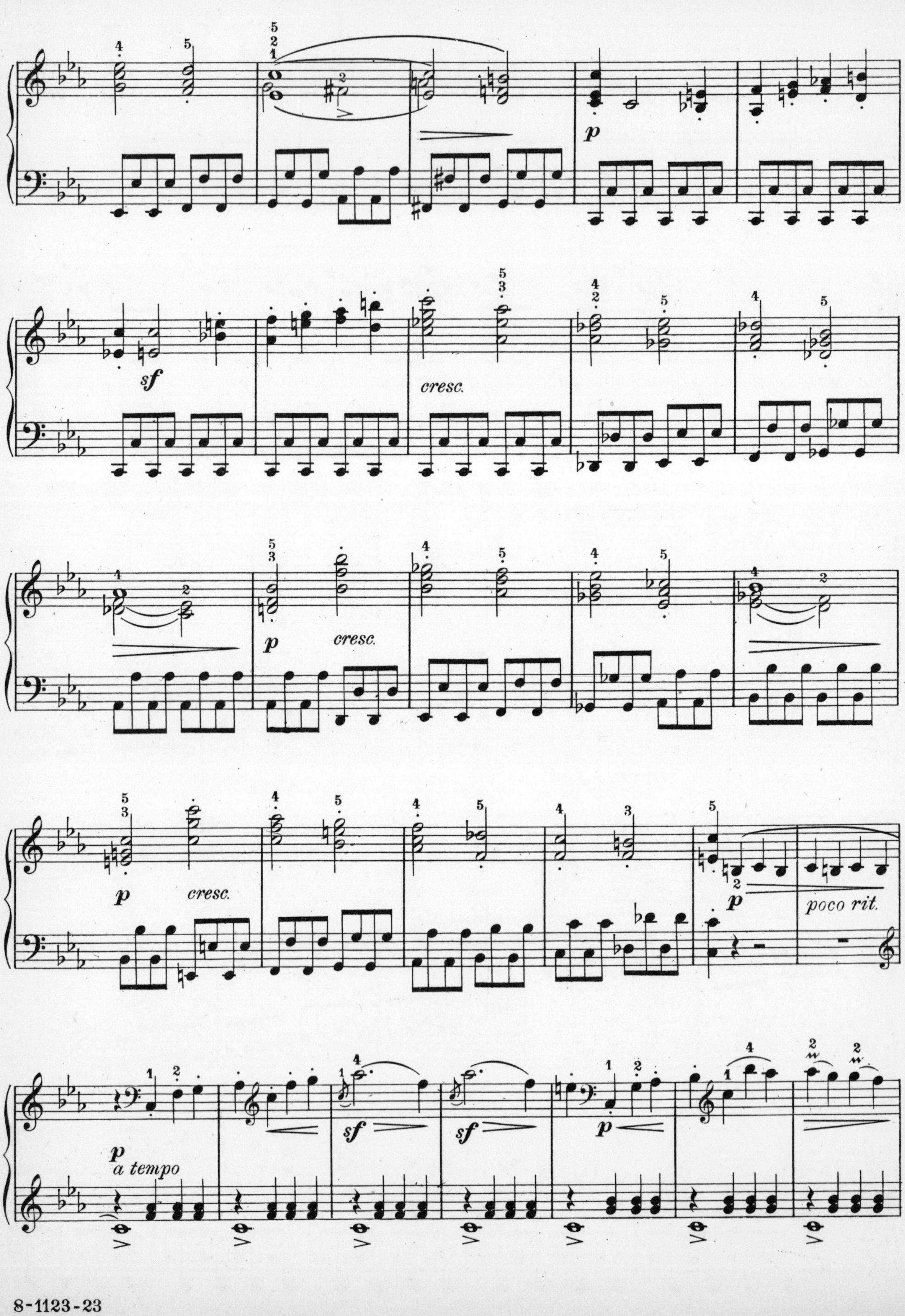
p
sf
cresc.
p
cresc.
p
cresc.
p
poco rit.
p
a tempo
sf
sf
p

1785

1786

1787

Adagio cantabile ($\eighthnote$ = 60)

1789

1790

1791

RONDO
Allegro

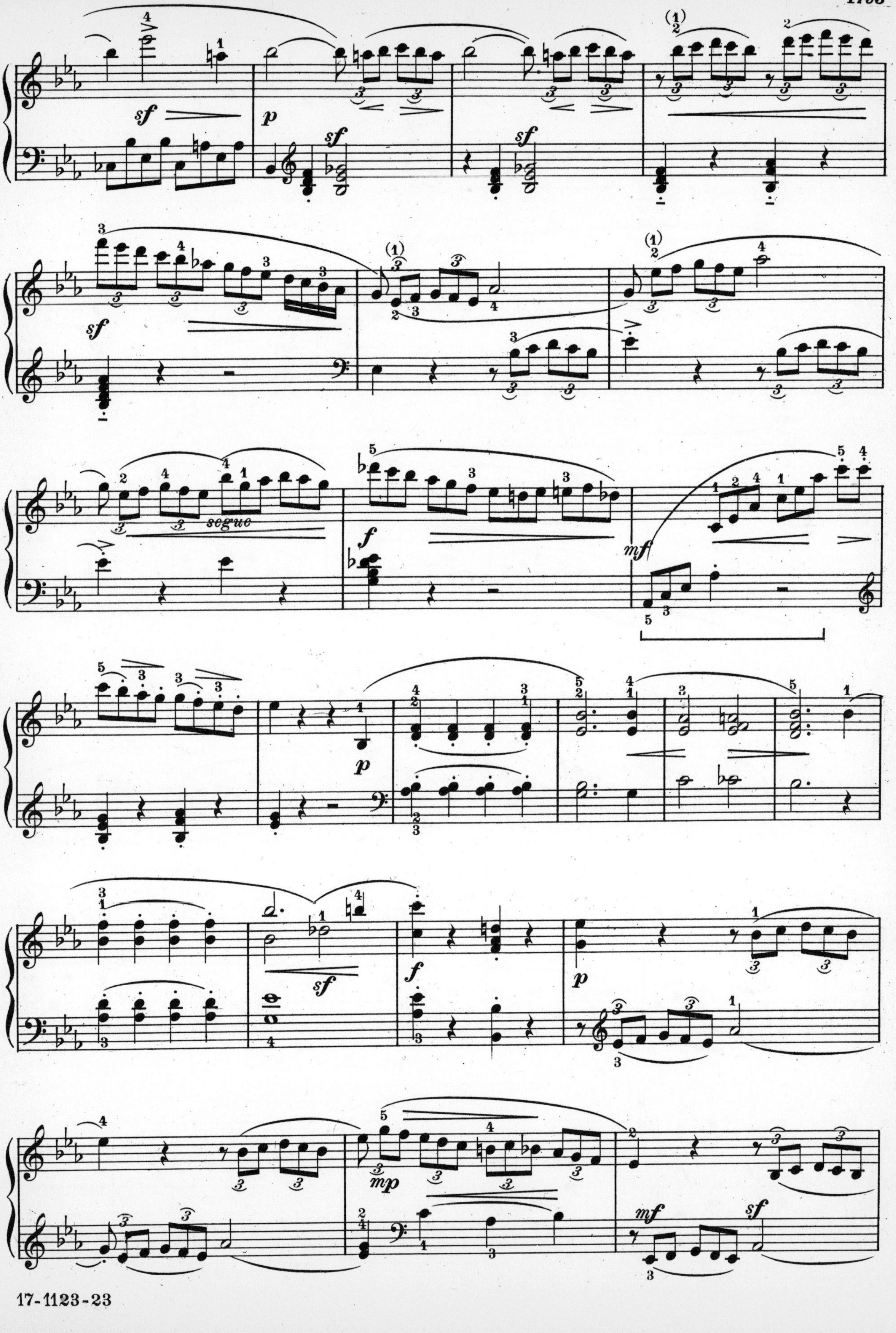
segue

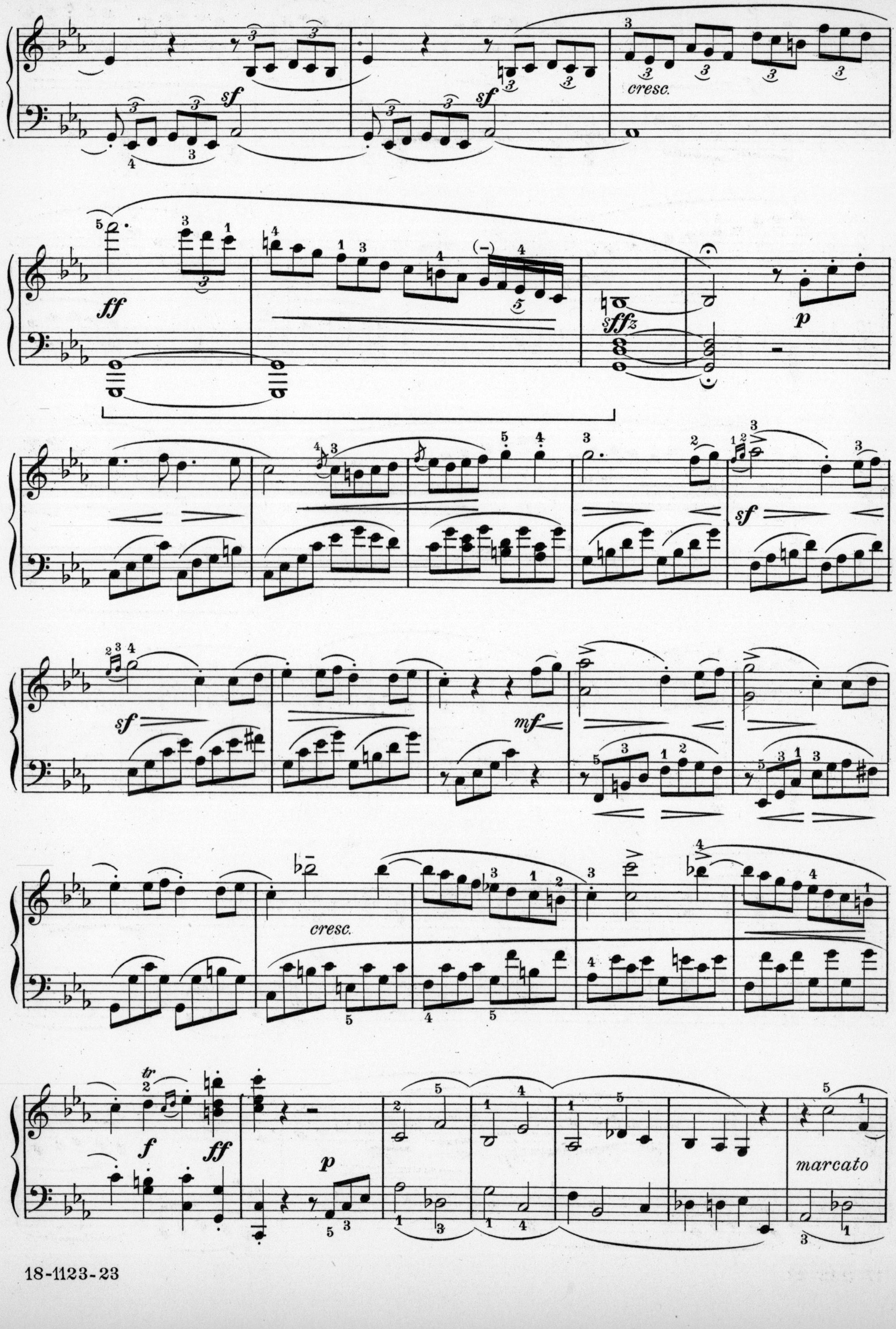
sf
sf
cresc.
ff
sffz
p
sf
sf
mf
cresc.
tr
f
ff
p
marcato

1795

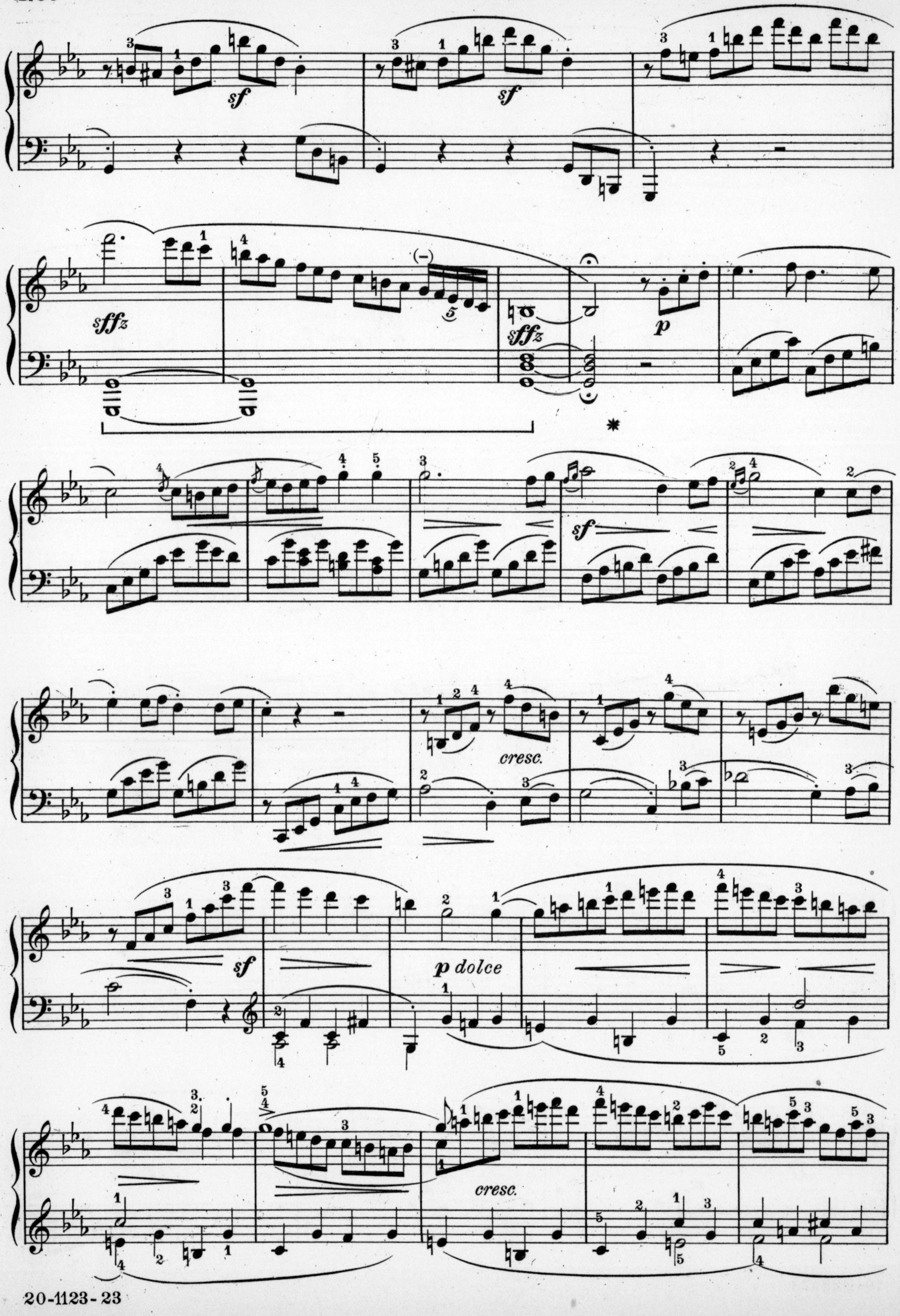
sf
sf
sffz
sffz
p
sf
cresc.
sf
p dolce
cresc.

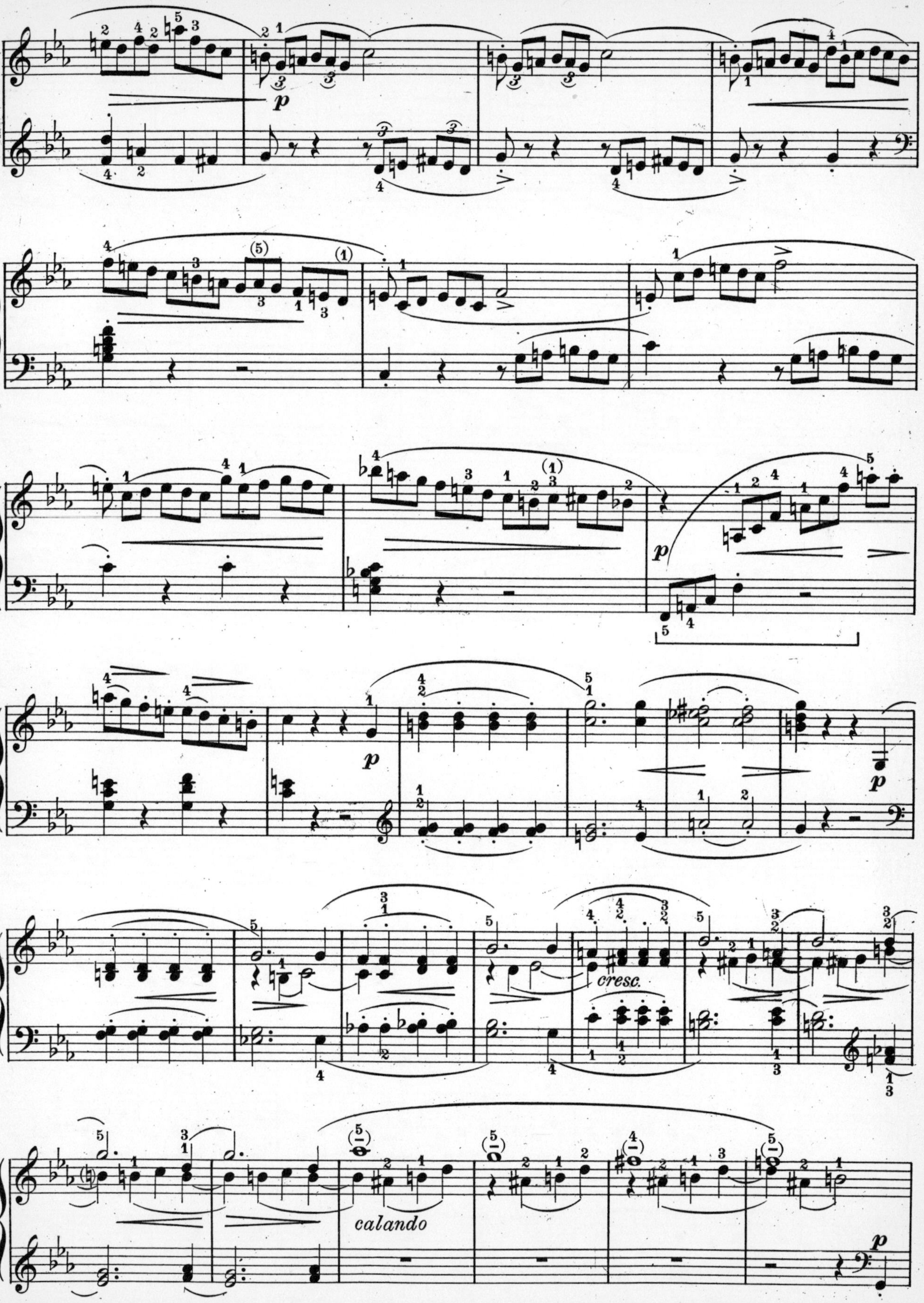
p
p
p
p
cresc.
calando
p

1798

1799

SONATA QUASI UNA FANTASIA
C-SHARP MINOR
"Moonlight"

Edited by Charles Dennèe

L. van BEETHOVEN
Op. 27, No. 2

Adagio sostenuto (♩= 50)

Si deve suonare tutto questo pezzo delicatissimamente e senza sordini

sempre **pp** *e legato*

pp *ma cantando con espressione*

Copyright 1918, by The University Society, Inc.

1801

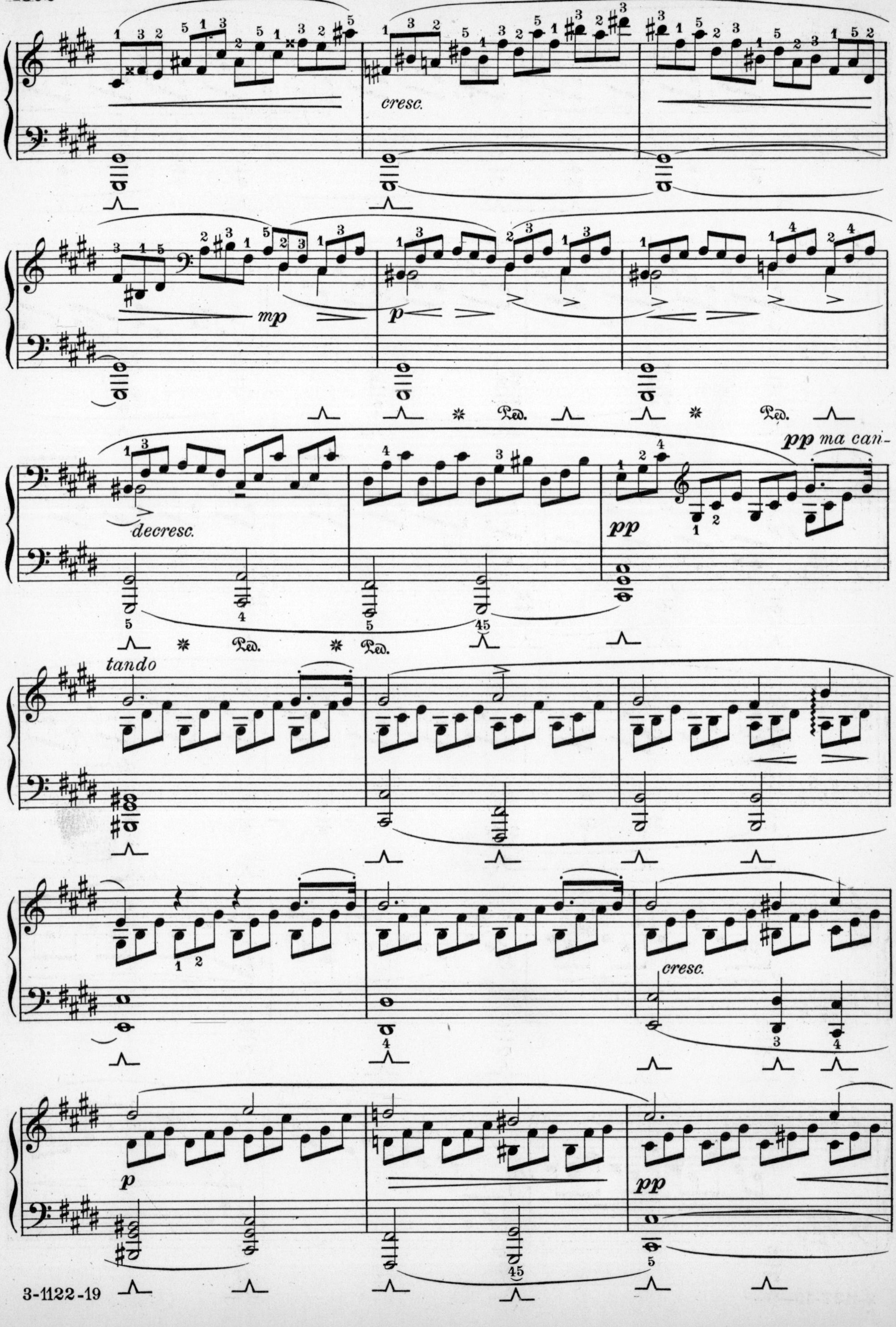
cresc.
mp
p
Ped.
Ped.
decresc.
Ped.
Ped.
pp
pp ma can-
tando
cresc.
p
pp

1803

Allegretto (♩. = 76)

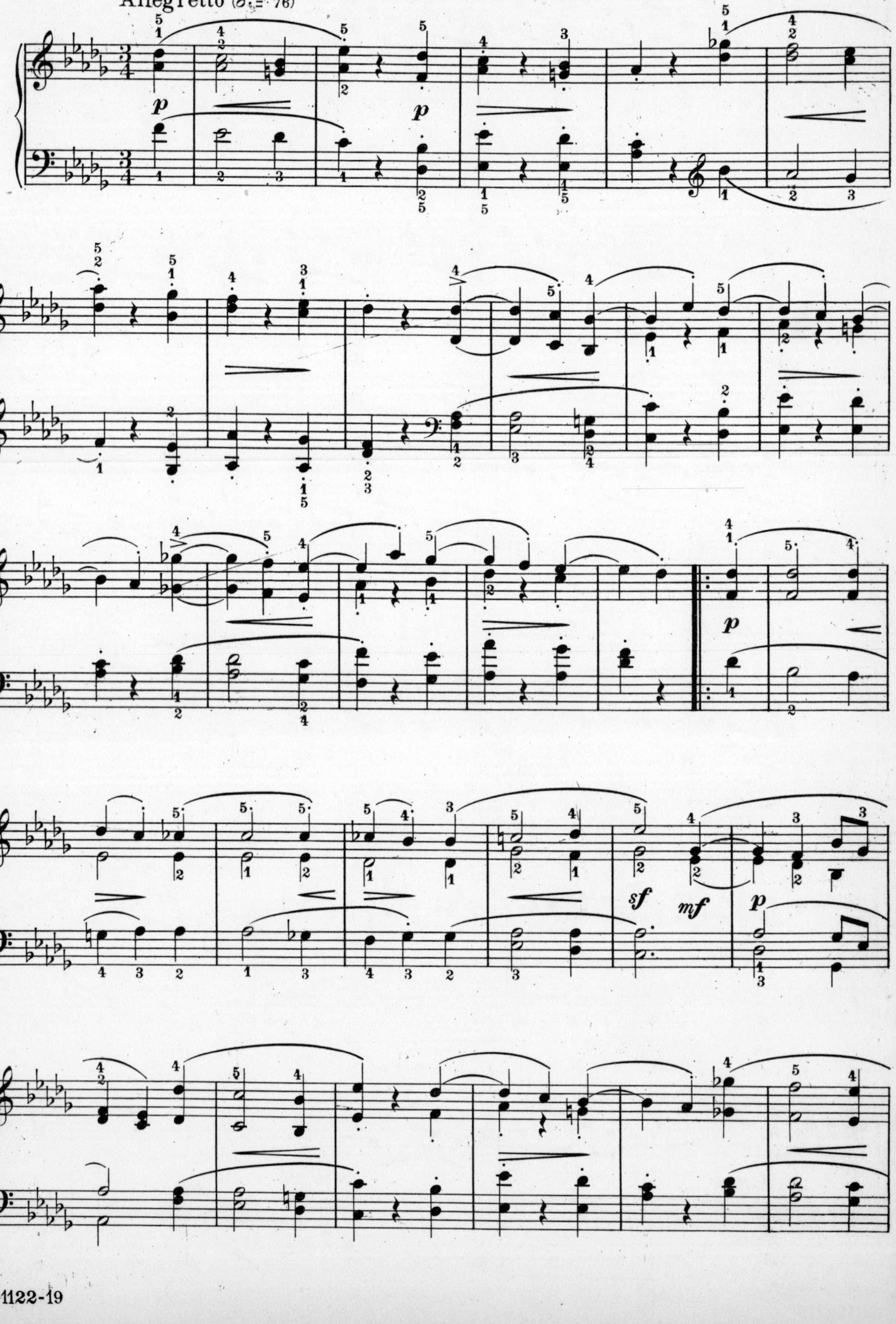

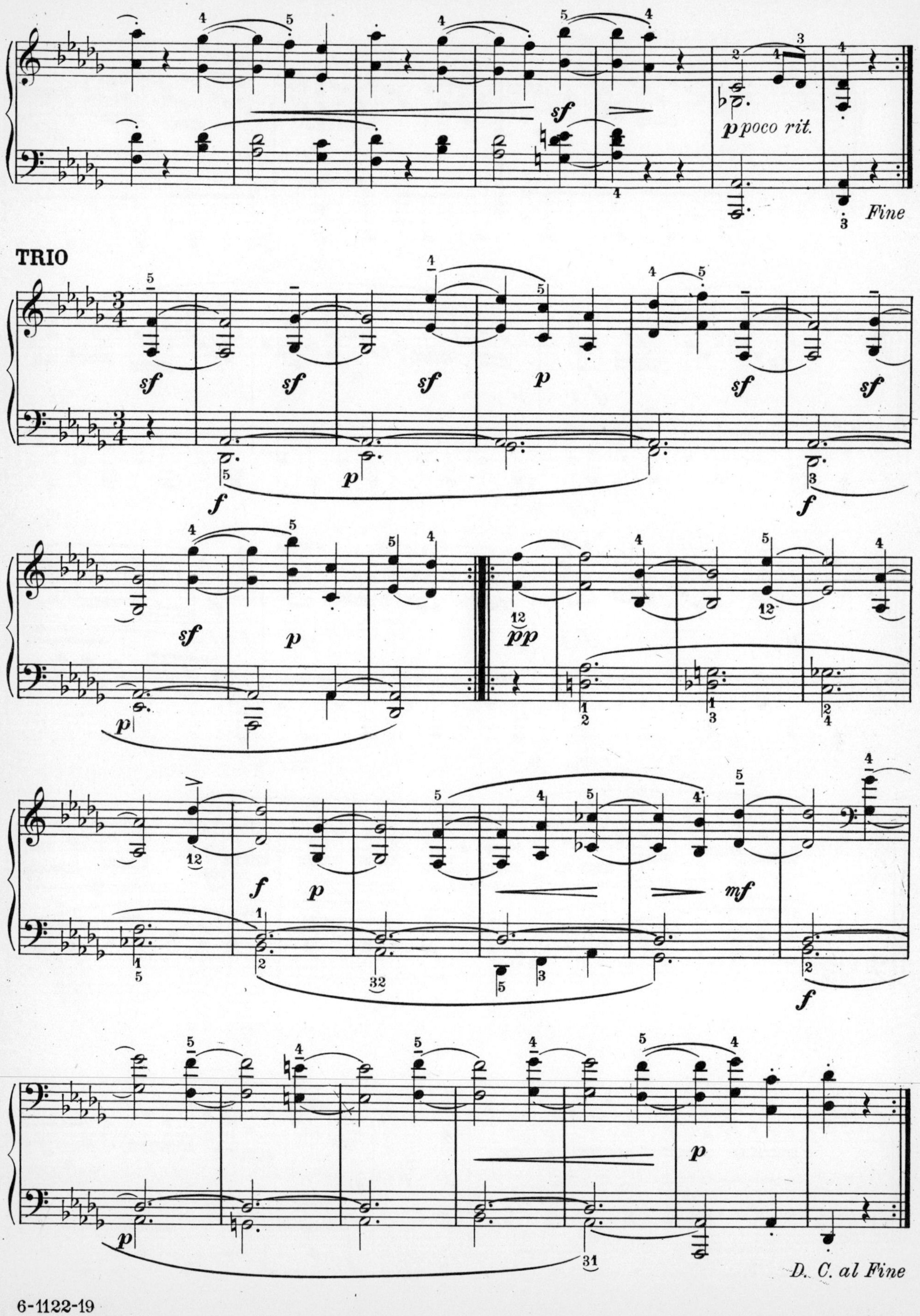
poco rit.
Fine
TRIO
D. C. al Fine

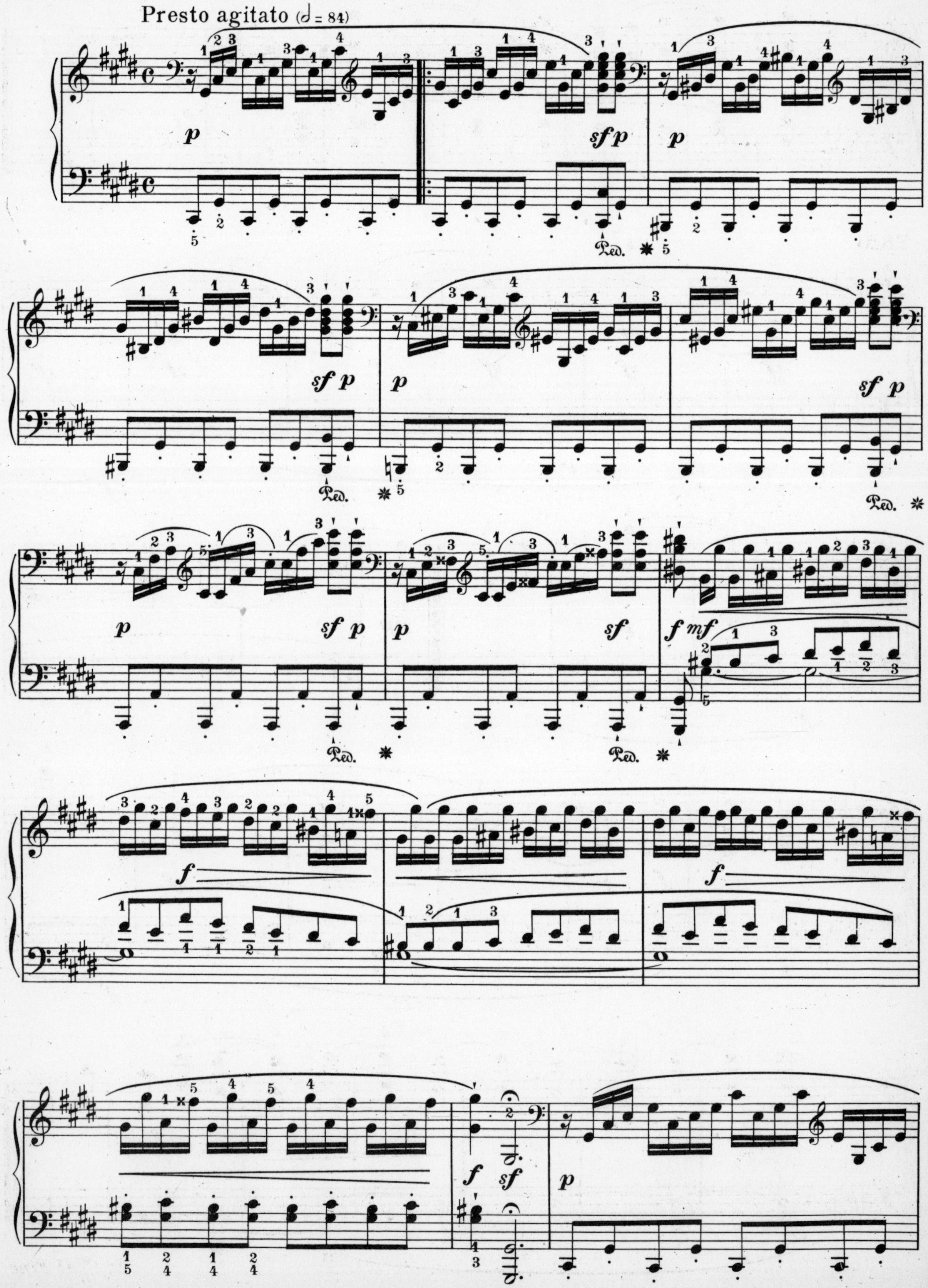
Presto agitato (𝅗𝅥 = 84)
p
sf p
Ped.
f mf
f
sf

1807

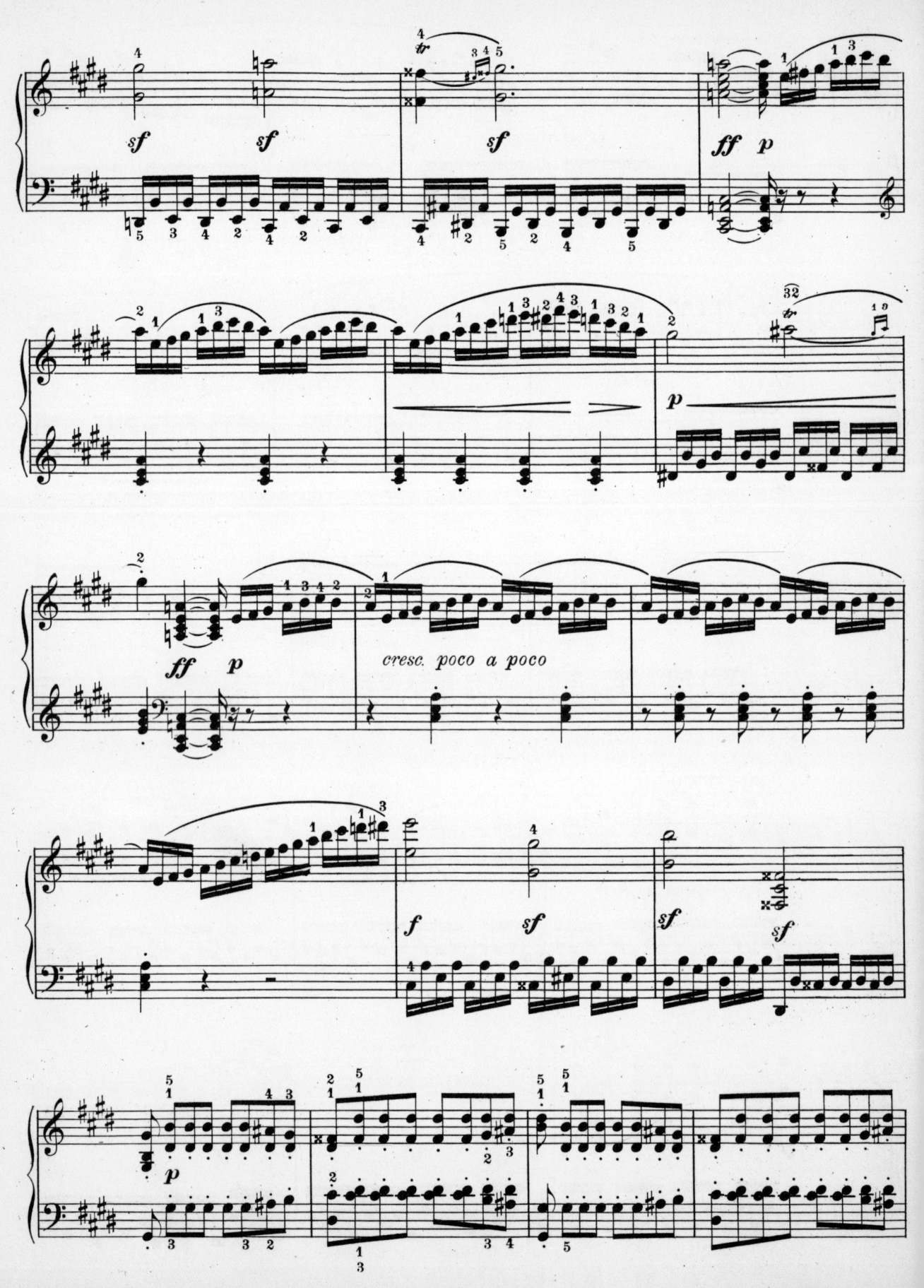
sf
ff
p
cresc. poco a poco
f

1809

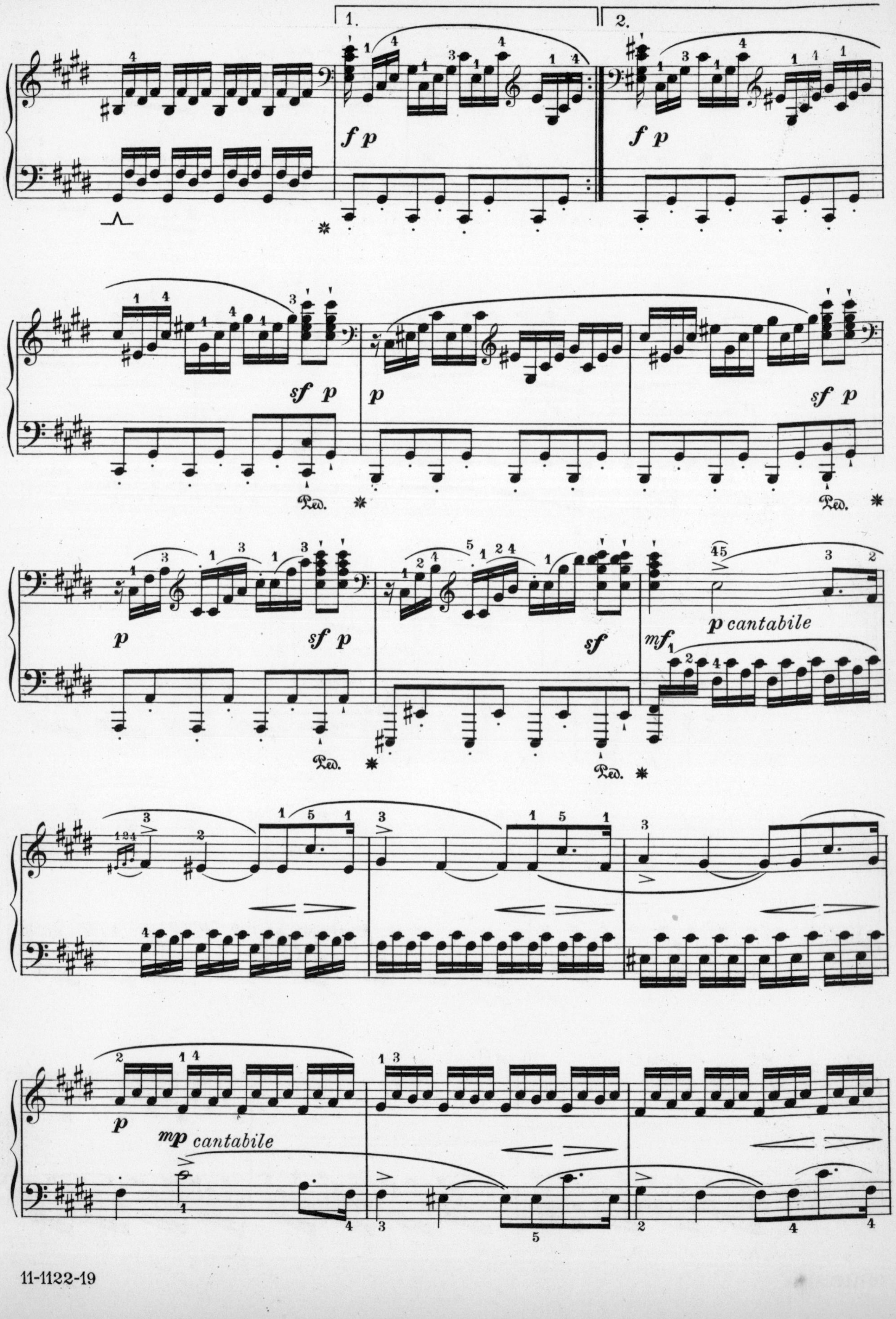
f p
f p
sf p
p
sf p
Ped.
p
sf p
sf
mf
p cantabile
p
mp cantabile

1811

1812

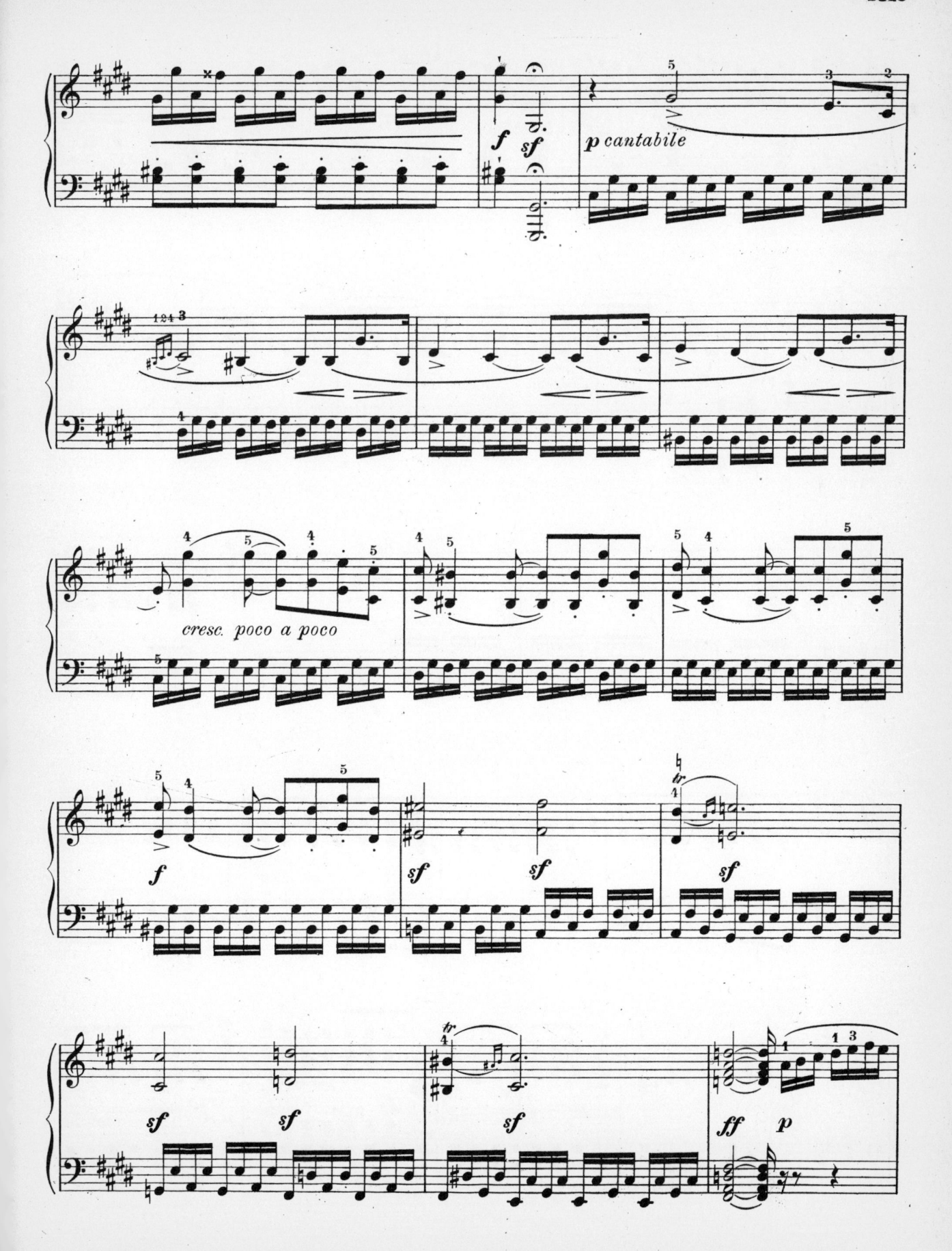
p cantabile
cresc. poco a poco

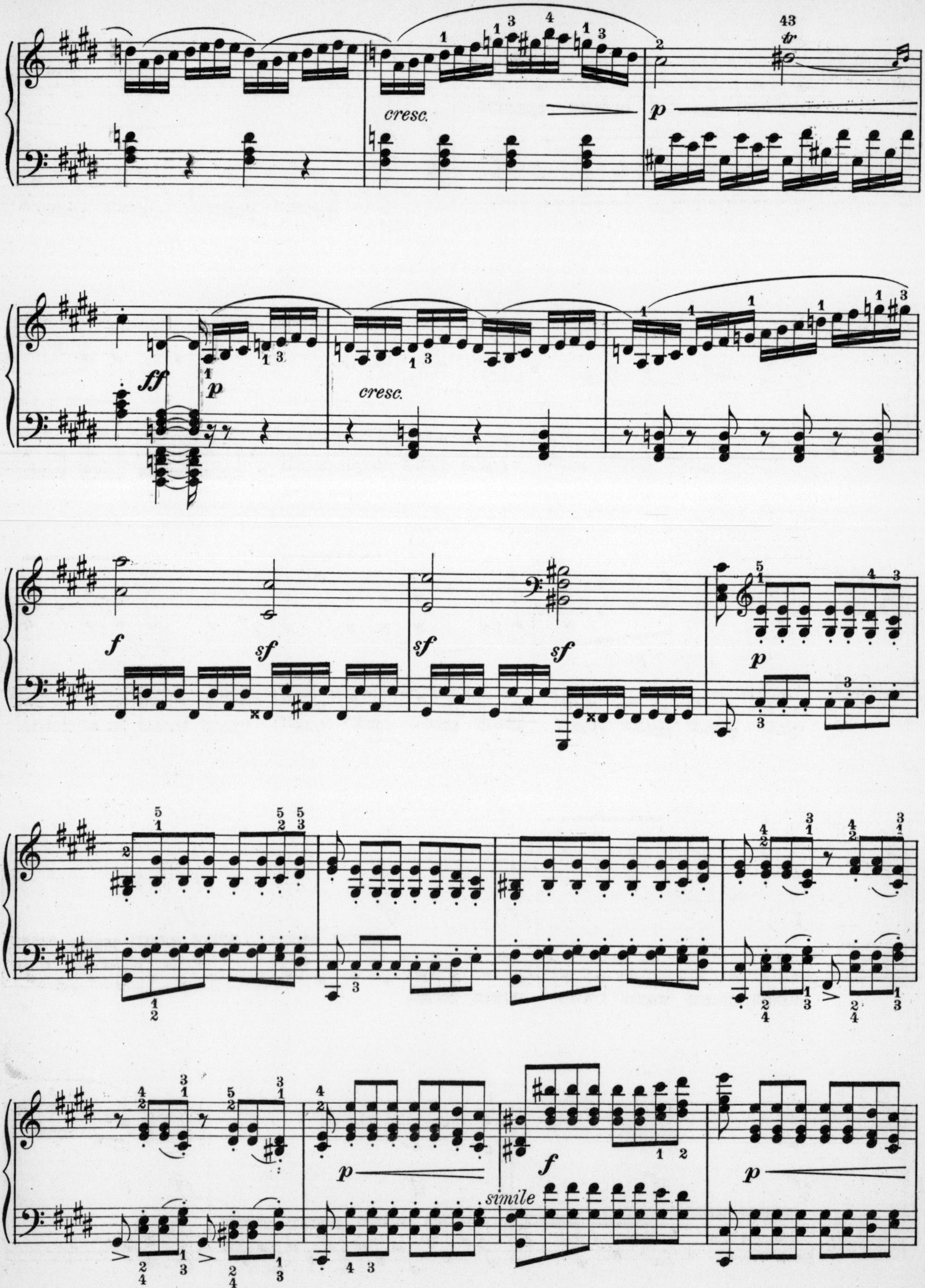
cresc.
p
tr
ff
p
cresc.
f
sf
sf
sf
p
p
f
simile
p

1815

1816

1817

Adagio
Tempo I.
f
mf
rapidamente
rit.
p
mf
cresc. e stringendo
un poco
f molto agitato
cresc.
f
ff

NOCTURNE
G-MAJOR

From the CENTURY LIBRARY of MUSIC
Edited by Ignace J. Paderewski

CHOPIN
Op. 37, No. 2

1820

1821

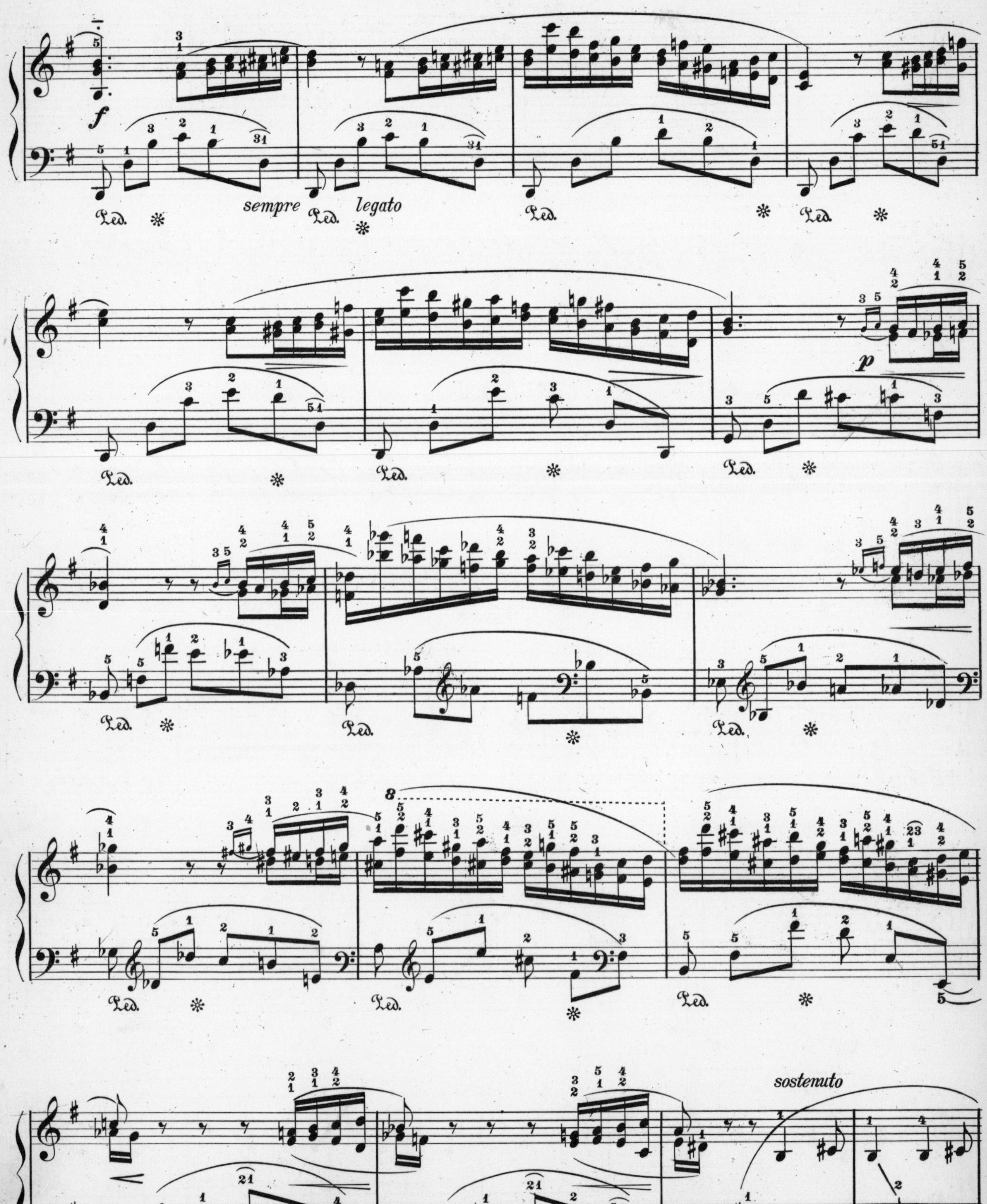
f
sempre legato
Ped.
p
sostenuto

1823

1824

The INTERNATIONAL LIBRARY of MUSIC

for HOME AND STUDIO